A Penguin Special
Seal Cull

John Lister-Kaye is an independent naturalist and writer who has concentrated on Scottish conservation problems for ten years. Since 1973 he has mounted his own study expeditions every year to grey seal breeding colonies in the Hebrides, in an attempt to make a personal assessment of this controversial and beautiful mammal.

He is founder and director of Aigas Field Centre in Inverness-shire, Britain's first private field studies centre, where he lives with his wife and three children.

JOHN LISTER-KAYE

SEAL CULL

THE GREY SEAL CONTROVERSY

PENGUIN BOOKS

Penguin Books Ltd, Harmondsworth,
Middlesex, England
Penguin Books, 625 Madison Avenue,
New York, New York 10022, USA
Penguin Books Australia Ltd, Ringwood,
Victoria, Australia
Penguin Books Canada Ltd, 2801 John Street,
Markham, Ontario, Canada L3R 1B4
Penguin Books (N.Z.) Ltd, 182–190 Wairau Road,
Auckland 10, New Zealand

First published 1979

Copyright © John Lister-Kaye 1979
All rights reserved

Made and printed in Great Britain by
Hazell Watson & Viney Ltd, Aylesbury, Bucks
Set in Monotype Times

Contents

List of Illustrations

The chess-board is the world; the pieces are the phenomena of the universe; the rules of the game are what we call the laws of nature. The player on the other side is hidden from us. We know that his play is always fair, just and patient. But also we know, to our cost, that he never overlooks a mistake, or makes the smallest allowance for ignorance.

Thomas Henry Huxley

Acknowledgements

I am most grateful to the many people who have assisted with the collection of information for this book and with its preparation. Irene Henderson typed its many drafts and, with Robert Graham, prepared the interview transcripts from tape recordings. Peter Wortham and Roy Dennis checked the manuscript and Sorrel Lister-Kaye, as well as conducting interviews and providing constant help and support, tolerated with sanguinity the great domestic upheaval the work has caused.

In particular my sincere thanks are due to those who agreed to be interviewed: Sir Frank Fraser Darling, Sir Peter Scott, Mrs Grace Hickling, Mr Nigel Bonner, Mr Alan Thornton, Mr Basil Parrish and the late Lord Cranbrook, whose knowledge and experience have much helped me to stabilize my own views. Mrs Hickling has kindly contributed photographs and the *Observer* is thanked for permission to reproduce Trog's cartoon. Dr Charles Summers is thanked for permission to quote from 'The Con in Conservation', which first appeared in the *New Scientist*, London, the weekly review of science and technology, 30 November 1978; the late Lord Cranbrook for the personal statement in Appendix 2; B. B. Parrish and W. M. Shearer for 'Effects of Seals on Fisheries' and B. B. Parrish for 'Notes on the Scientific Basis of the Fisheries' Case', reproduced in Appendices 4 and 5. Other assistance has come from Dr R. M. Laws of the British Antarctic Survey and Mr Bernard Gilchrist of the Scottish Wildlife Trust. Charles Barrington, Roderick Miller and Peter Wortham have greatly helped me to familiarize myself with Hebridean grey seals during the past five years.

Co-operation from the following bodies is gratefully acknowledged: the Fauna Preservation Society; the Society for the Promotion of Nature Conservation; the World Wildlife Fund; Greenpeace UK Ltd; the Scottish Wildlife Trust; the Scottish Society for the Prevention of Cruelty to Animals; the Mammal Society of the British Isles; the British Museum of Natural History; Department of Zoology, Aberdeen University; the Orkney Field Club; the Scottish Fishermen's Federation; the British Fishing Federation Ltd; Moray Firth Salmon Fisheries Co. Ltd; G. C. Rieber; the Nature Conservancy Council; the Department of Agriculture and Fisheries for Scotland; the Scottish

Office; the Natural Environment Research Council; the International Council for the Exploration of the Sea; the National Trust; the National Trust for Scotland; the Press Association; and B B C Radio Highland.

*

When writing about a subject which is in itself a conflict of ideas between individuals and organizations, it is inevitable that views expressed will be caught in a crossfire of professional opinion. I have taken great care to avoid misrepresenting anyone or any corporate policy and it should be understood that in essence the book is a strictly personal interpretation.

Aigas Field Centre   JOHN LISTER-KAYE
December 1978

Introduction

In October 1978 a towering controversy arose in Britain over a government seal cull in the Orkneys. Seal cull rows are nothing new. The Farne Islands, off the Northumbrian coast, have known hot opposition to their management programmes for years, and in the Gulf of St Lawrence the annual cull of harp seals for their pelts meets with an international upsurge of feeling. So the public of the Western world is tuned in to seal hunting and to seals, even though most people on both sides of the Atlantic will only ever see a seal on television or in a zoo, and, as far as they know, it will never conflict with their way of life. Why, then, should this passionate interest exist?

The answers are not logical or clear, but it seems to have something to do with the singular fact that seals give birth to a helpless pup which is quite unprotected by a nest, burrow, vegetation or even camouflage. To add to this helplessness its mother is badly equipped to protect it. Also, it is covered in soft fur to keep it warm in a horrible climate, and our Western culture loves all things young, furry and helpless. What has added more than usual fuel to the 1978 Orkney controversy is a new issue brought to the already disapproving public's attention by the appearance of the Greenpeace Foundation. This international conservation group had already made a name for itself in a brave bid to stop the killing of whales on the verge of extinction. Along with their presence in the Orkneys, and their own very individual style of confrontation with the contracted hunters, came the very reasonable request for one year's halt on the cull because they doubted the adequacy of the scientists' figures which justified the killing.

The media caught on to this new twist to the old humanitarian argument with fervour. It made exciting reading and excellent television, and the public was immediately fed with copious and conflicting statistics and opinion.

Within two weeks the story read like a thriller and the nation was captivated. There was a debate on it in the European Parliament in Brussels and it was clear that the affair was becoming an embarrassment to the Scottish Office, which had authorized the cull, and to the government at large.

On 16 October 1978, with some reluctance, Mr Bruce Millan, the Secretary of State for Scotland, announced that the programme had been halted because of public concern. The Norwegian seal-hunting ship employed to do the work was signed off and sent home, and new, far smaller, proposals were put forward. Now everyone is asking where we stand. What is behind the allegations that the figures concerning seal populations and damage to fish stocks have been cooked to suit individual parties' interests? And what is the truth behind the pointed suggestion that the Scottish Office and its scientific advisers don't really know what they are doing?

All fundamental issues in a democracy are decided by public opinion, but in order for that opinion to be meaningful it must be based on some firm foundation of fact or experience. One of the most striking features of this controversy is the absence of accurate figures. At the moment the man the street in Britain, and for that matter in most other countries on both sides of the Atlantic, is being forced into prejudice by the clumsy presentation of the evidence. This book attempts to present facts and arguments at variance in a straightforward manner in an endeavour to help the intelligent observer to make up his own mind.

Conservation is a principle which our world needs more and more as we continue to overcrowd and overpressure our fragile earth. The seal row is a conflict within conservation, and, for that reason, it is a crucial issue. More than ever before it is vital that the outcome of this controversy should be a rational and ordered solution for fish, man and seals. If it is permitted to become a sore of discontent the damage could be worldwide and pervasive. If the reader is looking for a clear-cut answer he will be disappointed; conservation is one of the most complex uncertainties in the history of man's relationship with his environment, and no author is in any position to produce clear-cut answers. Rather, it is hoped that by stimulating debate and reassessment of facts, motives and actions, at least the true issues will become clearer and better understood.

CHAPTER 1

Conservation – Killing and Cruelty

Seals costing fishing industry £25 million a year.
Daily Telegraph, 13 February 1978

The killing of 5,000 seals in the Orkneys is totally
wrong. If it goes ahead, nothing but shame will befall
Britain.
Sunday Mirror, 8 October 1978

I think a cull of government ministers is a better idea.
Correspondent in the *Sunday Mirror*, 15 October 1978

The seal kill is an attempt to shift the blame for
declining fish stocks from human over-fishing to seals.
Greenpeace statement, October 1978

Seals don't get fat eating grass.
Orkney fisherman, *Sunday Times*, October 1978

Seals are unquestionably beautiful animals. That much is clear,
and it is an important part of the controversy, but it should not
be the major principle on which the rights and wrongs of a conservation issue are assessed.

Conservation is a much used word, and in the seal row it has
been bandied about at will. It comes to us direct from the Latin
verb *conservo*, which means to maintain or to keep up. From the
noun *conservatio*, the act of maintaining or keeping up, we get
our noun conservation. Its meaning has not changed, and it can
still justifiably be used to mean the upkeep of traditions, cultures,
industries, sports or anything else. But in recent times the word
has been linked with natural resources so persistently that it now
immediately connotes wildlife, forests, rivers and mountains,
rather than buildings and other artifacts of man's existence. In
Britain we have called our first national agency for looking after

our wildlife and its environment the Nature Conservancy, and several other organizations concerned with the environment feature the word conservation prominently in their name. Because of this, and because on our crowded planet more and more conservation work has had to be concerned with the saving of rare and threatened animals and plants from extinction, in the minds of many people conservation has come to mean solely the prevention of killing of animals and destroying of habitats. This is mistaken, and it should be understood that in this book and in any informed use the word means the upkeep and management of whatever is in question. In fact it is certainly true that in order to manage some wild populations of animals properly, regular and systematic killing is necessary and an important part of practical conservation.

It is not a coincidence that the Latin word *conservus* means a fellow slave, one who serves alongside and is of equal status to another slave. I find it an attractive idea that we are all slaves on this earth, animal, plant and man together, all serving in equal bondage under the driving force of need. The need for food and a home are common to all living creatures, and, while some would argue that man's status on earth is no longer equal to that of his fellow animals, his need certainly is. In conservation – in serving his needs alongside his fellow occupants of the earth – man stands a very much better chance of survival than if he goes it alone. This is what the science is all about and it is a happy state of affairs that there is now a visibly growing awareness of the principles of conservation in our modern world.

Ironically, this controversy differs from any other killing issue in the subtlety of scientific opinion involved, which the general public could not be expected to make up its own mind on or research at all thoroughly. The issue has been confused with bloodsports, commercial exploitation and political intrigue, none of which is relevant. The irony lies in the fact that the Secretary of State for Scotland called off the cull of adult seals in response to the weight of public opinion against him – misinformed opinion induced by propaganda which played on the emotions of millions and presented little fact for intelligent consideration. As soon as the cull was abandoned the press dropped the subject like a hot stone and the public remains sublimely ignorant of what it was really all about. At the time of writing the argument continues only in academic circles, and even there a stalemate exists which cannot be overcome in the short term.

So, who are the goodies and who are the baddies? The goodies were seen by the public to be the conservationists, embodied in the romantic and swashbuckling Greenpeace men and several others who backed them up. The baddies, then, must have been the proposers of the killing, the Department of Agriculture and Fisheries for Scotland, and their advisers. That seems all very clear-cut. But on closer examination we find that while the goodies were preparing to throw themselves into the line of fire to save the lives of fellow occupants of our hallowed earth, the baddies were acting in what *they* considered to be the best interest of mankind, the fish in the sea, and even the seals themselves.

When this perplexing conundrum was revealed by the world press the public withdrew into a state of cataleptic indecision while television men and journalists rushed around the Orkneys interviewing fishermen and government officials, each one eager to uncover some new and decisive snippet of evidence. Meanwhile the humanitarians got to work with full-page advertisements in the national press, and dramatic pictures of wet-eyed seal pups patiently awaiting their execution. The man in the street had no alternative but to identify the wet eyes with those of his dog staring balefully up at him from the carpet beside the television, and in a matter of a few days the outcry was so great, the letters to the press and to government departments themselves, including No. 10, were so numerous and angry, that Mr Millan had to call it all off.

Gloating press coverage was given to the Greenpeace men drinking champagne aboard their now famous vessel *Rainbow Warrior*, and the Norwegian sealers hired to do the killing slunk quietly away into the North Sea mist with more than a hint of tail between legs.

It is not surprising that the public was largely misinformed. The difference between the policy of the government and that of their main opponents is very fine. One side says there is adequate scientific evidence that grey seals are eating too many commercial fish.

The other says there is not. The poor man in the street has no means of gauging the truth one way or the other. We shall examine both cases and their histories in detail later on, but for the moment it is sufficient to try to analyse the public response.

The scientific evidence exists in some bulk and in a completely indigestible form. Assessing its proper merits is a long and difficult task. As far back as 1969 Sir Dudley Stamp wrote in his careful analysis of Nature Conservation in Britain that it was clear from the start that seal-control policy was unlikely to please everybody. That was a masterful understatement, but I doubt whether even he imagined that the public interest would escalate as dramatically as it has. The allusion within Sir Dudley's bleak statement must refer to what is often called our humanitarian instincts, but which is more plainly expressed as sentimentalism. A letter to the London *Times* on 7 October 1968 points out that the seal cull issue is a particularly splendid example of the British character being kind only to *nice* animals. There is certainly truth in this statement, and its logic, whether the writer knew it or not, is clear.

Since man first stepped out of the primeval forest he has been a hunter and a fisherman. As well as his food he has needed wood for his fire, minerals for his tools and implements, and skins for his clothing. He still needs all those today, although along the way he has learned much about wise and unwise exploitation of the earth's resources, animal, vegetable and mineral. Farming was one of the first forms of conservation, because as man's population grew he realized that sooner or later he would run out of wild food plants and it was both practicable and necessary to help nature to produce sufficient for him. He was, for the first time, controlling his environment and managing its potential resource.

Before long, wild animals ventured out from the forest edge to sample the abundance of food plants growing in our primitive farmer's allotment. In anger and despair at the damage inflicted on his crop our hunter-farmer massacred the marauding animals by a concentrated hunt through the surrounding forest and he set traps for any foolish enough to venture back again. He had come into conflict with his fellow animals for the first time and he had to kill them not as a primary food source but as a control measure to protect his own livelihood.

For thousands of years the rapidly increasing numbers of men on the earth have been driving the wild animals back into the forests and felling the trees to expand their food-growing area to meet the needs of a larger population of men. We are still doing it, and it is a relatively new concept of land and animal management even to allow wild things to exist at all in conflict with man's interests. We have almost passed through the dismal eras of total exploitation, when commercially valuable animals and plants and minerals were hunted, felled and dug up until there was nothing left. Now, in a new dawn of enlightenment comparable to that which shed light into the lives of those men who first thought of farming, we believe that not only should we live and let live a little, but that we should keep a close check on our wild animals to see that they do not get too scarce or too numerous, and on our wild habitats to ensure that there is enough space for the wildlife to exist in.

This is not the dizzy brainchild of some super intellect, although it has taken some mighty thinking to put it into practice. It is the product of necessity. In the thinking world where we do not have to hunt and scrape the soil for our daily food, we have realized, perhaps too late, the awfulness of our position. Conservation is not just a better thing to do, it is a vital need if life is to exist for men as we have come to like and enjoy it.

The snag is the extent of the thinking world. There is a serious difference between ourselves in a Western civilization and what is called the third world, but which might now more appropriately be labelled the fourth, fifth and sixth worlds as each new sub-continent breaks into the technological era. In all those countries where the population lives a subsistence existence from day to day, struggling on the edge of starvation and battling hopelessly with disease, the vast majority of the people are primary food producers. Their life is a constant process of toil and sleep, each day's labour barely guaranteeing food for the following day. There is no time in their lives for any aesthetic consideration, and the idea of nature conservation, if they have ever heard of it, is totally alien to them, representing only less food and less space to grow it in.

In our world the position is reversed. The primary food producers – the farmers and fishermen – are a very small minority of the population. But although they have a far higher standard of living and are conscious of aesthetic values, they have to contend with exactly the same natural hazards as the farmers of the third world. They are just as prone to climatic vagaries ruining their harvests or wrecking their fishing boats, and to the invasion of agricultural pests, whether it is deer, rats, weeds, insects or seals. To this minority group, nature conservation is an accepted principle because their standard of living is high enough for them to be able to appreciate the aesthetic, philosophical and scientific reasons for it; but they do require of it that it must not seriously conflict with their economic interests or damage their life style.

The rest of our population, the huge majority of our industrial society, are largely urban and suburban dwellers, also with a high standard of living, who have very little or no contact with the environment and its wildlife, except – and here is the crux of the situation – through the aesthetic ideology of literature, television and the media and their whole cultural heritage which stems from a previous rural era before industry and suburbia were even thought of. The office or factory worker returning to his comfortable home at the end of a day's work has the time and the money to indulge in the exercise of critical faculty. The environment and its wildlife are presented to him as beautiful and spiritually uplifting co-inhabitants of his world. Wonderful books and films, magazines and television in super-colour all play on his emotions, suggesting powerfully that there is a better life in the country than in the office and the urban sprawl, and plucking at a need most of us feel deep down when we are separated too long from the soil and the countryside of our agrarian ancestors.

In his leisure time our industrialized man spends his money in the rectification of these inadequacies and the pursuit of enthusiasms gleaned from the media he has been exposed to. He digs furiously in the soil of his back garden and grows food plants and flowers, balancing his aesthetic sense and his need to link himself with country life. That done he crams his family into his motor car and sets off to find the countryside for himself. He looks to the agencies of nature conservation, and the government, and to the clubs and societies he may join and identify with, to protect the environment and its wildlife which he needs to re-charge his spirit and assemble his values.

What is only very rarely revealed to our modern industrialized man is that there are still serious conflicts between nature conservation and the production of the food he by now takes for granted in his local supermarket. He sees a wheat field full of poppies and corn-marigolds as only beautiful, and has no sympathy for statistics which show the reduction in corn yield because of weeds. He sees the rabbit and the deer as the rightful occupants of the woodland and the thicket, and, if the farmer is foolish enough to plant sugar-beet in the neighbouring field, then he deserves to have them eaten. He has no truck with blood-sports, which have evolved from our basic hunting instincts (unless it is angling, which is by far the most popular field sport in the Western world), and the need to control pests, and he scrutinizes the destruction of agricultural pests with a heavy frown because the realities of death and cruelty are no part of his sheltered and civilized existence. Since the industrial revolution town man and country man have been growing steadily apart and developing increasingly different life styles and values. It is one of the major problems facing government today. Is the country to be run on industrial community standards because they are the majority, or are votes to be thrown away by recognizing the importance of conflicting minority needs? The problem becomes worryingly complex when governments realize the importance of minority needs and the electorate doesn't. This is the position of the grey seal controversy.

Fishermen are primary food producers in a small minority. A mere twenty-five thousand people are employed in Scotland directly and indirectly by the fishing and fish-processing industry. Fishermen see a rapidly expanding population of seals eating more and more fish, some of which he knows are commercially valuable to him. They convey this worry to the government, who set up a research team to investigate the truth in these allegations. Rightly or wrongly, as we shall examine later, they decide that something must be done. They take careful advice and follow it. Suddenly the majority of the population, fed copious stimulating literature by the media, sees the killing of grey seals as vandalism putting at risk the heritage of the wildlife they are just beginning to enjoy and causing a good deal of suffering and cruelty in the process. The weight of their opinion brings the whole programme, which set out to be an active nature-conservation management measure for the benefit of everyone, to a grinding halt.

Coldly assessing the tactics used by both sides, it was clear that Greenpeace would win infinitely more public support than the government. The whole battle was skilfully manoeuvred by Greenpeace, who launched a clever public relations exercise and made use of the sympathy already won by the humanitarian lobby, which, at least at this stage in the analysis, is not an important standpoint. 'Greenpeace' and '*Rainbow Warrior*' are profoundly romantic labels designed to appeal to the man in the street. 'The Department of Agriculture and Fisheries for Scotland' connotes only bureaucracy and red tape. The presence of the brightly painted ship in the Orkney Islands made excellent television, whereas the low profile of the government spokesmen aroused no great journalistic fervour.

By 14 October the newspapers were struggling to find new material to report on the deadlock. The popular heroes of animal welfare had, in fact, achieved a considerable goal already. The cull had been postponed because of the controversy and the presence of Greenpeace. Time was running out for the cullers. It was now clear that even if they started shooting seals straightaway, and the weather remained calm, they would find it very difficult to kill the full quota of seals in what remained of their contract with the Scottish Office. The one propaganda move the Secretary of State for Scotland did instigate backfired straight away. In an interview for radio and television Mr Millan reaffirmed his belief that the scientific evidence for the cull was sound, and then tried to swing public opinion against its opponents by claiming that their activities on the island of Muckle Greenholm had been damaging to the seals. The Scottish Office suggested that between fifty and a hundred pups had been deserted by their mothers because of the disturbance of protesters. He condemned this and announced that experts would have to go to the island and humanely kill the orphaned pups.

It was an ill-conceived move from the onset. First of all the impact on the public was negligible, and, when it did register, the universal response was one of scorn. Journalists lost no time in pointing out that this degree of concern for the welfare of a few seal pups was not consistent with the Scottish Office plan to kill most of the pups on that island anyway. Whether or not the concern was bogus, it certainly sounded it. To make matters worse, when Mr John Prime, a scientist from the Sea Mammals Research Unit, and representatives from the RSPCA and SSPCA, went to the island to despatch the orphans they found only five abandoned pups and they were already dead. This figure was abnormally low even for a year with no disturbance, and it was also noted that there were far fewer breeding seal cows on the island than was expected from the figures for previous years. When this shortfall was also blamed on the presence of the protesters, Mr Prime, whose work has contributed to the evidence for the cull, was reported in the *Daily Mail* as saying: 'Well, this [disturbance] is quite a good way of keeping seal numbers down – it is actually done intentionally in the Farne Islands.'

It began to seem that the protesters could do no wrong. When on Sunday, 15 October, the Sunday newspapers appeared revealing still massive coverage of the issue, largely angled in favour of Greenpeace, and the correspondence columns groaned with the weight of conflicting opinion, it was clear that the programme could not proceed without doing real damage to the government's public image. It was not a surprise when on Tuesday, 17 October 1978, a spokesman for the Scottish Office announced in Kirkwall that the Secretary of State for Scotland had ordered a dramatic reduction in the numbers of seals to be culled, and had terminated the Norwegian contract without a shot being fired.

Predictably, the Fishermen's Federations were angry at the decision and spoke out against it straightaway. Members of Parliament whose constituents were allied to the fishing industry were also obliged to complain, but it was significant that of all the fishing constituency MPs around our coasts, only one made a really serious protest. Even he attracted little attention from the press. The subject was dead news. The drama was over. Public indignation was quelled and honour satisfied, even though up to two thousand pups had yet to be killed by local Orkney seal hunters under the reduced proposals ordered by the Scottish Office. So, in this instance, the opinion of an independent conservation faction prevailed over that of an official conservation force through the reaction of a largely sentimentalist public. Before considering whether this is a good thing for seals or fisheries, or conservation in general, it is only fair to examine the humanitarian argument.

One of the growing gaps between town and country life is the level of exposure to death and the processes of decay which will inevitably follow it. We all live by standards of conduct and appreciation which are instilled early in life. The town boy or girl playing in an urban environment is unlikely to come across dead animals at all regularly, and if a child finds a dead sparrow, for instance, and carries it attentively home to a parent for explanation, the outcome is likely to be some expression of exaggerated sympathy for the departed bird, or even disgust, suggesting that death is abnormal or distasteful. In the country a child will be brought up in regular contact with this reality and after a very short time will accept as normal the dead hedgehog squashed on the road or the dead mouse in the lane. Moreover, in truly rural areas the child is likely to be reared against a background of regular killing – the local shoot or hunt, the farmer shooting rabbits, the rats and mice around the house being trapped and poisoned and, perhaps most important of all, the inevitable acceptance sooner or later that all farm livestock will eventually be killed for humans to eat. This last concept is often entirely missing from the urban child's understanding of the natural order of things, and it may come as something of a shock when it finally dawns that all the sausages, chops and roasts displayed in the supermarket are actually the self-same farm animals as those idealistically depicted in children's books.

Although, of course, adults know very well about the killing of animals for food they very often choose not to think about it very deeply. This is especially true of town folk and so, when suddenly presented with killing of any sort, they react instinctively in accordance with their own instilled standards. It is at this point that the word cruelty first appears.

It is a common misconception of our society that cruelty is any killing or any pain. It is, of course, an essentially human concept anyway and cannot possibly be attributed to the animal kingdom.

The natural killing of any prey by any predator outside the influence of man is entirely without cruelty, regardless of the level of pain or suffering inflicted. Nature is savage. Killing is a prerequisite of birth and procreation both as a food source and a natural control of population. Almost no wild animal dies of old age. Virtually all living things are eventually going to be eaten by something else. This is how our life-support system on earth is designed and there is nothing we can do about it even if we wanted to.

What, then, is cruelty? Cruelty is man causing unnecessary pain or suffering on anything, be it man or beast. It can be inflicted either by intent or default. It is just as cruel to beat a dog unnecessarily as to forget to feed it. If a bird with a broken wing lies unseen in the yard, no cruelty has taken place, but if a man comes along, sees it suffering, and does nothing about it, then he is guilty of cruelty by default. Humane killing – killing quickly and efficiently with the best intention to avoid suffering – is not cruelty. It is the opposite. The proposal to kill seal pups humanely is no more cruel than the proposal to take lambs to the slaughterhouse. The standards carefully laid down for both are quite devoid of cruelty, as will be seen in a later chapter. An element of suffering may creep into any killing operation and it should be guarded against, but even so, unless the human responsible is intentionally negligent, he cannot be held to be guilty of cruelty. These facts are straightforward and basic, but unfortunately they are not commonly understood, as our own public opinion researches have revealed and as a glance at the correspondence columns of the national press during the controversy will endorse.

In the light of this, any newspaper, radio or television authority or any society or association which has deliberately allowed public emotion to be stirred by the suggestion that the control measures proposed by the Seals Advisory Committee are cruel, is guilty of irresponsible interference and ignorance. Anyone bothering to read the humane recommendations and standards which have been in existence for many years, and the research which went into their compilation, will quickly discover that this aspect of the exercise has been most commendably covered. And it is acutely relevant that the Chairman of the Seals Advisory Committee,

Lord Cranbrook, is also responsible for such pertinent legislation as the Animal Cruel Poisons Act, which provides for the humane destruction of rats, for instance, at a time when the public could not have cared less how a rat died.

Consequently, because I believe that such sentimentalism has no place in the rational examination of this sort of conservation issue, I have intentionally withheld mention of any organizations seen to be openly parasitic upon the public intellect in this way. On the other hand the all-important humanitarian standpoint is adequately and responsibly represented by the Scottish Society for the Prevention of Cruelty to Animals (because it is essentially a Scottish problem). Few of us would be slow to admit that the killing in cold blood of young and helpless animals of any kind, but especially animals as appealing in appearance as seal pups, is anything but distasteful and a task many people would not be able to bring themselves to perform. Discussing this recently with a scientist who has contributed greatly to our knowledge of seal population dynamics, I was told that, despite his keen interest in the programme, after several years of having to kill adult and young seals alike for scientific examination, he found it more and more degrading, so that finally he became sickened and left the field of seal research altogether.

Nevertheless, the unfortunate fact remains that the issue was won by the use of the weight of sympathetic opinion much of which was swayed only by the heavy sentimentalism seals attract. Although in this case the result may not have been wrong, it is a bad principle that an important conservation issue should be so affected by uninformed opinion. It can only make future seal control programmes here in Britain and elsewhere more difficult. It may also affect the rationale of other important decisions. But it does make it quite clear that good public relations is a vital exercise for government and independent bodies alike.

CHAPTER 2

The Orkney Countdown

Archaeological finds and the written history of our islands has given us an idea of how grey seals have affected our existence and development in Britain. When man first colonized these islands after the retreat of the last ice age, some 12,000 years ago, it seems certain that the grey seals were here first. They may have been very numerous and they may have been less protected than they are today, breeding commonly all round the mainland and island coasts. Man has almost certainly driven them out to remote stormy isles by constant predation for skins, oil and meat. They were probably the most important single source of life-support needs available to that first, late, stone-age culture. It is not surprising that, more than any other mammal, the seal – the selchie, as it is known – has won a foremost position in the folklore and legend of the Gaels, the Orcadians and Shetlanders. It has been afforded a mystical quality of human dimensions and in some areas is still believed to be the reincarnation of fishermen drowned at sea.

The story of man's involvement with the grey seal in Britain is most easily presented in table form:

Iron and Bronze Age in Scotland c. 1600 BC	In the iron-age and bronze-age kitchen middens of Jarlshof, at Sumburgh on mainland Shetland, the bone remains of grey seals have been found. Bones have also been recovered from sites of early man in the Hebrides and the Western Highlands. It seems most probable that seals were a vital aid to the colonization of man in the Western Highlands and Islands when he first appeared, probably from Ireland, as a stone-age shore dweller, eating fish and shellfish and other coastal prey.

Ninth–Tenth Centuries	We know from the considerable Viking history contained in the Icelandic and Norse sagas that seals were important to Vikings, for skins, sea-boots and tunics, for oil, and for fresh meat on many of their constant island forays around our northern coasts.
1549	The first record of sealing on the Hebridean island of Haskeir as an annual harvest for islanders from Lewis and the Uists.
1758	Sealing is referred to as a regular industry on Haskeir by Rev. Kenneth Macaulay.
1786	The first record of annual sealing expeditions every Martinmas to several Orkney breeding colonies.
1792	Seal skins for sale in Stromness, Orkney, at 2s. 6d. each.
1828	The Sobieski Stuarts report the use of a particularly foul gadget which was commonly used for the commercial killing of seals until about this date. It seems that the general scarcity of seals because of the heavy level of predation at this time caused the method to disappear. 'It was . . . practised with much profit by the fishermen upon the low sand banks, where the seals resort to bask and sleep, when they are left dry by the ebb-tide. Along the seaward side of these haunts, secured sufficiently to prevent them from rising with the water, they laid down large logs of timber, into which were bolted a number of strong barbed clips (spikes), the points of which, being directed inwards, allowed the seals to pass over towards the shore without injury; but, upon their return outwards, impaled them on the opposing hooks. When a number of seals had collected on the banks the fishermen gave the alarm from the shore, upon which the herd hurried to-

wards the sea, and, scrambling over the logs, were caught upon the clips, and held fast until the arrival of their enemies, who dispatched them with their clubs.' This method would undoubtedly have caught grey and common seals alike.

1838   MacGillivray records up to 120 seals killed on Gasker, off the Isle of Harris, in one day.

1848   'Upon most of the coasts of Scotland the seals are now considerably diminished,' write John and Charles Sobieski Stuart in *Lays of the Deer Forest*. 'Their former celebrated haunt, the island of Haskeir, has been much decreased by long and continual slaughter and upon many of the mainland banks they have completely disappeared. The greatest numbers now remaining are upon the isolated rocks . . . and caves in the coast of Sutherland and Caithness. In all these haunts, however, their pursuit is a churlish butchery and not any chase allied to the noble art of venerie . . . One of the most remarkable of those sea-dens . . . lies a short distance to the south of the old castle of Wick; its access is by a beach which slopes upward from the sea, and is said to penetrate three hundred yards within the rocks. In a prolific season the cave is sometimes crowded with seals, when it is dangerous to attack them, and at all times the assault requires much activity, dexterity and experience. The instant that the boat touches the beach at the mouth of the cavern, the men leap quickly to shore, and, armed with short clubs, range themselves on each side of the entrance close to the rock, and as much as possible out of the "run". The seals are sometimes alarmed too soon, and charging down to the sea, upset and "score" all who are in their way; those [seals] which are struck on the nose immediately fall senseless, and the rest, as they follow, scramble over the prostrate bodies and are then easily killed. Upwards of a hundred have thus been slaughtered in one morning; but some of the men are, occasionally, severely cut by the fugitives and novices are often grievously punished for their awkwardness or inexperience. One of those . . . was overwhelmed by the tumbling mass of snouts, and paws, and tails, and rolled away towards the water. After the seals had passed, it was with great difficulty, and severely scored and bruised, that he was drawn out from beneath the heap of monsters which had been killed above him, but to which he owed his life; for, had he not been covered by the lifeless bodies, he would have been carried by the tumult into the sea.'

1858   Sir John Orde, the proprietor of North Uist, puts a stop to the annual slaughter of seals on Haskeir by the Uist islanders. It is thought that he did this on humanitarian grounds because the reports are of particularly bloody clubbing of adults and pups alike. In any event it was a forlorn gesture because men from the isle of Lewis immediately took over the killing.

1880   Harvie-Brown reports regular sealing from Hysgeir off the island of Canna. That great advocate of Highland field sports, John Colquhoun, who must be the arch-predator of that predatory era, writing on seal shooting in *The Moor and the Loch*, advocates the seal as a noble quarry, whose pursuit is to be accomplished by 'all who would wear the hunter's badge'. He then launches into a series of sickening anecdotes of his own endeavours. Of the seven seals he kills three are shot and retrieved and the other four disappear. About those he does kill he admits surprise, since the range was so great and the target, a bobbing head, so small that he quite expected to miss or maim, and the others he confesses to shoot-

ing at unreasonable range so that wounding them
was also very likely. 'I fired at three in line, and
must have hit a pair of them, for we traced two
tracks of blood to the sea . . .' And then later, at
over 150 yards, '. . . I heard the ball strike . . . true
to the aim. Its companions dashed into the sea, but
the wounded seal rolled about on the sand, and
then struggled after them. When in the water, in
place of only the head, the whole disabled shoulder
rose above the surface, and the dives were short
and laborious.' (It would appear that the standards
of sporting gentlemen at that point in the great Vic-
torian sporting era had reached a particularly low
ebb and bear little relation to those of the Sobieski
Stuarts writing even half a century earlier.)

1882	30 seals killed on Sulsgeir.
1883	107 seals killed on Ronay (North Rona).
1884	143 seals killed on Ronay.
1885	89 seals killed on Ronay. Reports from R. M. Barrington and Harvie-Brown.
1913	Mr Hesketh Pritchard reports that the Haskeir seal clubbing still goes on every autumn, although seal stocks are now seen to be very low.
1914	The first preservation measure in Britain. The 1914 Grey Seal Protection Act was passed, providing a close season from 1 October to 15 December each year. (It was suggested that at about this period grey seal numbers in Britain might have been as low as 500, but in the light of later population estimates this is seen to be a very low figure.) The Act was only intended to give protection for five years, since even at this stage it was realized that the situation could change quickly.

1927   Professor James Ritchie and Mr W. L. Calderwood
              make a population estimate around Scotland (but
              excluding the Orkneys, the Shetlands and the
              Farnes) at between 4,000 and 5,000, with 1,000 pups
              born each year.

1929   In *The Times* of 8 January that year appears an
              anonymous letter pointing out that ignorance of the
              Grey Seal Protection Act was widespread and that
              the annual slaughter on Hebridean Islands still
              went on. Rae, writing of this in 1959, states; 'The
              clubbing of grey seals is a brutal affair. The fisher-
              men sail for the seals' island nursery by night to ar-
              rive there at daybreak. Grey seals resort to some
              outlying island where they bear their young. The
              young are land animals for the first few weeks. They
              are born above the reach of the tide, sometimes 50
              feet above the sea, and there they remain, helpless.
              In the early morning the mothers suckle them; and
              on landing the fishermen guard the passes so that
              the old seals shall not escape. With wooden clubs
              the men strike at the parents as they move clumsily
              toward the sea. Some of the mothers refuse to leave
              their babies and lie beside them, roaring and moan-
              ing, until they are dispatched. The baby seals are
              easily killed, and thus are far more fortunate than
              those which are overlooked and left motherless to
              die a lingering death. More seals are slaughtered
              than can be carried away, and the following season
              their carcases can be seen lying on their isle.'

1932   A new seal population estimate of 8,000 appears at
              this time. The Grey Seal Protection Act is amended
              to extend the close season by six weeks from 1 Sep-
              tember to 31 December. Special powers are also
              granted to the Minister of Agriculture and Fisheries
              and the Secretary of State for Scotland to suspend
              the close season for the purposes of control. Lord

Strathcona and Mount Royal, himself an island grey seal colony owner, was instrumental in the effecting of this legislation.

1934   177 grey seals are killed on the Cornish coast to appease fishermen. (Not only was part of this done during the close season, which flagrantly broke the law, but, almost worse, none of the corpses were made available for scientific examination.)

1938   A conference is held at Newcastle-upon-Tyne to debate the damage grey seals were doing to fisheries.

1939   The publication of *A Naturalist on Rona* by Frank Fraser Darling. This was the first serious attempt to study a grey seal breeding colony in depth, and included the first protracted stay on such a remote island as North Rona.

1955   'A Joint Committee on Grey Seals and Fisheries' is set up by the Ministry of Agriculture and Fisheries and the Nature Conservancy. From this date the Nature Conservancy provides grants to natural history societies and universities for the much needed research into seal biology and behaviour.

1959   The first Farne Island cull on record. In order to allay pressure of complaint from the salmon fishing industry a cull of moulters was done. But, for the first time, there was an adverse and largely misinformed public reaction, and as a result the National Trust, owners of the Farne Islands, refused permission for any further control measures.
        A team of four scientists visit North Rona from 1 to 26 October, the first visit since 1938.

1960   Mr E. A. Smith is appointed the first full-time seal researcher by the Joint Committee of the Ministry

of Agriculture and Fisheries and the Nature Conservancy. Working from the Nature Conservancy
headquarters in Edinburgh, his first significant
achievement, in the course of affecting a census, was
to discover that the hitherto unimportant Orkney
grey seal populations were in fact massive. In October of that year the first experimental cull was carried out in Orkney. It was done by rifle marksmen
under the supervision of a veterinary officer from
the Home Department of the Scottish Office. The
two islands controlled were Wartholm and Little
Greenholm, and, because it was not yet known what
method of control was likely to be the most effective, a cross-section of bulls, cows and pups were
shot. This was especially advantageous because the
corpses were badly needed for scientific examination and they did provide what can be considered
the first adult material in breeding conditions from
one colony, giving an age distribution which has
subsequently been proved to be largely correct.

Throughout the sixties the Scottish section of the
Nature Conservancy was responsible for work on
North Rona, a National Nature Reserve in their
charge. Under the leadership of Dr J. Morton Boyd,
himself an important grey seal researcher, an immense body of information was gathered by tagging
and branding and by the annual monitoring of that
Reserve, which is also the largest island colony of
grey seals in the world.

1962   The publication of *Grey Seals and the Farne Islands*
by Mrs Grace Hickling, an important milestone in
publicly available grey seal literature.

1963   The Consultative Committee on Grey Seals and
Fisheries, funded by the Development Commission,
produces its first report (largely from Mr E. A.
Smith's researches) under the chairmanship of

Dr E. B. Worthington (*Grey Seals and Fisheries*, HMSO, 1963). This report made firm recommendations for the control of grey seals and underlined the need for continued research.

From the recommendations of the 1963 report the Minister authorized an annual pup cull in Orkney which was intended to reduce the 1963 estimated population of 10,500 by 25 per cent over the next few years. The whole Scottish population of grey seals is estimated at 29,500 at this time.

1965   The formation of the Natural Environment Research Council. Responsibility for funding seal research was now handed over from the Development Commission. A Seals Research Division was set up to work from the Fisheries Laboratory at Lowestoft. This meant an increase in manpower and facilities which permitted more accurate counts using air survey and high-speed boats. Furthermore its remit included all aspects of seal biology and not just those affecting fisheries.

1970   The Conservation of Seals Act 1970 reaches the statute book. Lord Cranbrook, then President of the Mammal Society, prepared and introduced a Bill for the Conservation of Seals into the House of Lords in 1968. It was defeated on the second reading, but Lord Shackleton, spokesman for the government, offered for the preparation of an amended Bill. In 1970 Lord Cranbrook tried again with a private member's Bill and succeeded. In essence the Act provides for close seasons for both species of British seal during their breeding seasons while allowing for the Ministers concerned to license seal culling for the protection of fisheries interests, for the support of the commercial sealing industry and for the collection of material for scientific purposes. It also stipulates what weapons are to be used.

Under the Act the Natural Environment Research Council has the duty of advising the Minister on the management of seal populations, and consequently the Seals Research Division and the Seals Advisory Committee are appointed and set up to enable NERC to fulfil this obligation.

1971   The appearance of *Grey Seals and the Farne Islands – A Management Plan*, by W. Nigel Bonner and Grace Hickling. This document was produced for the owners of the Farne Islands, the National Trust, as a recommendation for the conservation of the whole environment of the islands. Because of overcrowding the seals were suffering high pup mortality, and disease. Some islands were losing their vegetation and soil covering because of the seals, and bird and insect species were also decreasing as a result of the rapidly expanding grey seal usage. The plan recommends stabilizing the Farnes colony at 1,000 breeding females, and achieving this by shooting adults as well as the removal of pups. Recommendations are also made for control measures to be carried out on breeding sea birds damaging the soil structure of some islands.

1972   132 bulls, 603 cows and 573 pups culled on the Farne Islands as a conservation measure. Widespread public concern was expressed. The carcases were extensively used for scientific research.

1973   In spite of annual pup culls since 1973 carried out every year the Orkney breeding population had grown to an estimated 12,500 animals, an increase of 2,000 seals in ten years. The whole Scottish grey seal population is now estimated at 54,000.

1974   The publication of Professor Hewer's *British Seals* in the Collins New Naturalist series. This is the first book published in Britain which gives an accurate up-to-date account of the biology of both grey and common seals, outlines the conflicts of both species with man's interests, and sets the scene for control policy. The death of Humphrey Hewer not long after his book was finished, and the loss of his knowledge and authority, is still held to be a bitter blow to seal biology and research.

1975   158 bulls, 486 cows and 804 pups culled on the Farne Islands as a conservation measure to protect the vegetation and wildlife of the islands. There was again a public outcry about this control, and again the carcases were used to produce valuable information about the age structure of the breeding colony.

1976   The Natural Environment Research Council produce their review of present knowledge in a comprehensive document by W. Nigel Bonner entitled *Stocks of Grey Seals and Common Seals in Great Britain*. The review contains an appeal for a continuing programme of research not only on numbers of seals but also into our understanding of seal behaviour.

1977   The start of the six-year control plan. The Norwegian firm G. C. Rieber is contracted to effect a cull of 4,000 seals in the Hebrides. There is little comment in the press and no active opposition. In October the Norwegian sealing vessel arrives in the Hebrides and immediately hits bad weather. She sails to the Monach Isles, but in three weeks of contract she is able to work for only three days because of savage storms. The Norwegians take no risks and eventually kill only some 600 seals, made up of adults, pups and moulters. The cull is considered to be a failure.

1977
November
13 bulls, 121 cows and 209 pups killed on Farne Islands as a conservation control measure. In spite of annual pup culls carried out every year since 1963 the Orkney breeding population had grown to an estimated 14,500 seals, an increase of 4,000 seals in twelve years. The whole Scottish grey seal population is now estimated at 60,000.

1978
13 February
The year starts with a glimpse of what was to come. A piece in the *Daily Telegraph* of Monday, 13 February was headed 'Seals Costing Fishing Industry £25 million a Year'. That particular outburst had little to do with Orkney. It was aimed at the National Trust, owners of the Farne Islands, by angry fishermen, for not reducing the grey seals on the islands by as many as would have been liked in 1977. The Sea Fisheries Committee in Newcastle estimated the daily fishing consumption of a grey seal to be up to 35 lb. That estimate was probably wildly exaggerated, but the fisheries lobby needed bargaining power and at that time only a handful of people in the country did know what a grey seal's diet was more likely to be. Then followed a lull.

1978
6 July
On this quiet summer morning, adequately in advance of the statutory forty-eight days' notice required to be given under the Act, the Scottish Office in Edinburgh issued a press notice. 'Mr Bruce Millan, MP, Secretary of State for Scotland, has announced his decision to go ahead with the cull which is planned in accordance with a co-ordinated plan drawn up in 1977 for the years 1977–82, on the advice of the Seals Advisory Committee of the Natural Environment Research Council. 'Licences for shooting with approved firearms will be issued for a total cull of 900 adult breeding females and their associated pups and 4,000 moulted pups of which 450 adults will be taken in Orkney and 450

adults and 500 moulted pups in North Rona by the Norwegian firm of G. C. Rieber, who are being engaged on a contract by the Secretary of State. The remainder of the pups will be taken by local hunters from Orkney and the Western Isles.'

After outlining the justification for the cull the notice closed with a direct quotation from Mr Millan: 'I recognize that many people throughout the country hold strong views on the subject of seal culling. However, I hope that all concerned will recognize that I am responsible for exercising statutory responsibilities, and I am satisfied on the evidence that action is necessary.' If Mr Millan imagined that the British public could be placated by so toothless an appeal as that, he was to be rudely disillusioned later on.

In the sources of scientific advice which he used, the diet of the grey seal has dropped to a daily 15 lb. instead of the Newcastle Fisheries' 35 lb. The seeds of confusion were being sown in the public mind.

1978
1 October

No indication has yet been given to the world when the cull is to start, but ground intelligence in Orkney has passed word to the Greenpeace Foundation that things are moving. Relatively little excitement is attached to the arrival of *Rainbow Warrior*, the Greenpeace trawler with a crew of five and fifteen volunteers aboard, in Kirkwall. They were in plenty of time.

1978
3 October

In Edinburgh Greenpeace and the Department of Agriculture and Fisheries for Scotland meet face to face. A notice appears: 'It was explained to the Foundation's representatives that the Secretary of State's decision to carry out a further cull this year is based on the advice of the Seals Advisory Committee and was taken after consultation with the Natural Environment Research Council and the

Nature Conservancy Council, both of which bodies will be co-operating in the cull as part of an integrated programme.'

1978
8 October

Forces of opposition gather in Kirkwall. Appeals to the Secretary of State for Scotland have apparently failed. In a public reply to letters of protest from Mr Jo Grimond, M P for Orkney and Shetland, Mr Bruce Millan reaffirms that 'The arrangements for this year's cull, which I announced as far back as 6 July, are now complete and I have authorized the operation to go ahead.'

A protest petition of 42,000 signatures, including 1,500 Orcadians, is delivered to the Scottish Office. Still no sign of the Norwegian sealers. Despite this the Sunday papers have major features on the brewing storm: '"Fight on the Beaches" Call to Stop Seal Cull' (*Sunday Telegraph*); 'Battle Lines Set in the Seal War' (*Sunday Times*). A prominent editorial appeal to the Prime Minister appears in the *Sunday Mirror*: 'Come on, Jim: Stop it!'

1978
10 October

A debate in the European Parliament on seals. Mr Finn Gundelach, Commissioner for Agriculture, promises that a neutral study on seals and their effect on fish stocks would be conducted, although the Commission would not attempt to halt this year's cull.

1978
12 October

Deadlock. The Norwegian vessel *Kvitungen* and the *Rainbow Warrior* lie side by side in Kirkwall harbour. There are angry clashes between government officials and protesters on the quay and a television helicopter causes a new row because it frightens pregnant seal cows into the water.

In Strasbourg an emergency motion put forward by Mr Tam Dalyell, Labour M P for West Lothian, which calls on the E E C Commission to halt the culling of seals until a scientific investigation has been carried out, is approved by the European Parliament.

1978
15 October

Sunday newspapers still full of seals. The cull has now provided one of the longest-running stories of the year. Still no progress. Protesters claim they have delayed the cull, government officials claim they are not ready to start anyway. The Norwegians are clearly fed up with the whole affair. The issue achieves major political cartoon status with Trog's

'Eat Jim's fish, would you?'

contribution to the *Observer*. During the week a bomb scare gives the whole issue a new and sinister flavour. The Norwegian vessel *Kvitungen* is threatened and the presence of undesirable-sounding frogmen is reported from Kirkwall. Happily, it comes to nothing, but an inspection of the boat's hull is made.

1978
16 October

A press release from the Scottish Office, announced in Kirkwall, breaks the stalemate. 'I have decided . . . to reduce the size of the cull this year so that everyone will have the opportunity to study the scientific evidence . . . I have decided to withdraw the Norwegian firm.'

By the morning of 17 October every national

newspaper has the cull in its main headline: 'Seal Cull Cut Back'; 'Greenpeace Victorious'.

The reductions *are* dramatic, from nearly six thousand adults and pups down to two thousand pups only. The reason given is the existence of 'widespread public concern'.

CHAPTER 3

Grey Seal Facts

The grey seal is scientifically known as *Halichoerus grypus*, which means Roman-nosed sea-pig. It was first described by Fabricius in 1791 in Greenland, who called it *Phoca grypus*, the Roman-nosed sea-dog, but it was later separated from other members of the true seal family, the Phocidae, and given its own distinctly prosaic genus. In 1820 Millson produced the generic name Halichoerus, which simply and somewhat unkindly means a sea-pig (Greek *halios* = sea, *choiros* = pig). *Grypus* had apparently stuck and so the current classification was approved. In 1851 two zoologists, Hornschuch and Schilling, tried to change *grypus* to *macrorynchus*, long-nosed, and then *pachyrynchus*, thick-nosed, but the subtlety was too fine and *grypus* remained. In 1886 Mehring tried to distinguish between the two then known European varieties of grey seal, calling them *atlantica* and *baltica*, and this distinction stands, although true sub-specific status is not yet accepted.

DESCRIPTION

Seals are carnivores and have a true meat-eater's dentition comparable with other land carnivores like wolves, dogs and cats. Like the dolphins and whales, they were once land mammals and have taken to the sea to live. Unlike the cetaceans they have retained an ability to return to land to breed and to moult or to just lie about. They also have four clearly defined limbs complete with claws and fingers, whereas the cetaceans have become so specifically adapted to ocean life that they bear little resemblance to land mammals.

The first primitive seals probably emerged some 10–20 million years ago, it is thought, from dog-bear ancestral stock. As well as being Britain's largest carnivore, the grey seal is our largest mammal. Quite unlike some of the small seals of the world which, at a pinch, one could pick up and carry, the grey seal is considerably larger than the largest man. Even the fairly trim females weigh up to about 29 stone (186 kg) in peak condition, and the gargantuan bulls can achieve some 49 stone (310 kg) – a mammal far larger than the biggest red deer stag.

They are covered in short, close fur which varies greatly in colour. There is a generalization of slate blue-grey, but often the cows are dappled and patchy all over, with a mixture of cream and orange and silver. The bulls tend to be more uniform but can also be distinctly sandy right through to almost black. The pups are born in a coat of long white fur which is only fast for about four days, after which it begins to fall out and is replaced by a much shorter second coat of dappled silver-blue-grey. By far the most important features of recognition of the grey seal in British waters are the size and the Roman nose. While our common or brown seal has a distinctly dog-like or even otter-like face, the grey seal, especially the bull, has a long straight profile with no forehead, and a wide flattened brow.

DISTRIBUTION

There are three populations of grey seals: Western North Atlantic; Eastern North Atlantic; and Baltic. As far as is known there is no interchange of animals between the three populations and they can be considered as quite separate. It may even be that when specimens have been procured from the Canadian and Baltic areas, close examination will reveal sufficient differentiation to warrant the sub-specific classification attempted in 1886.

In recent years much information has appeared from research into all three populations, and, partly through improved census methods, and partly through the development of computers used for the calculation of exponential population forecasts, it is now considered that a fairly accurate assessment of the grey seal's world status has been reached. It was as follows in 1977:

The Western and Eastern North Atlantic populations are expanding healthily, but the Baltic population seems doomed. It has been found that because of human predation by bounty hunting

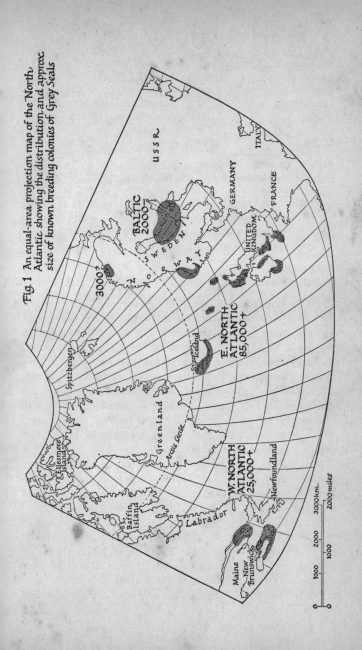

Fig 1 An equal-area projection map of the North Atlantic showing the distribution and approx. size of known breeding colonies of Grey Seals

Canada	24,000		
Iceland	1,000	**WORLD TOTAL**	
Faroes	3,000	108,000	
Great Britain	70,000	(This total appears to be	
Ireland	2,000	increasing by about 5 per cent	
Norway	3,000	per year.)	
USSR	3,000		
Baltic	2,000		

(ICES report, 16–20 May 1977 CM 1977/N:11)

and the presence of pollutants in the fish and the water of the Baltic, causing sterility in breeding females, the birth rate has dropped alarmingly. It is doubtful whether there are sufficient animals for that population to exist for very long.

HABITAT

It can be generally said that in Britain the grey seal belongs to rocky coastline, and the common seal to muddy and sandy areas. Certainly there are concentrations of common seals in areas like the Wash, while grey seals are to be found in numbers around the rocky coasts and islands of the Farnes, Hebrides and Orkneys. It is thus broadly true that the grey seal is an animal of the west coast of Britain, and the common seal of the east. But, though that generalization is frequently made, it is misleading. Both seals overlap throughout their range and grey seals are just as partial to a nice sandbank as common seals are to rocks. In fact they regularly haul out together on both.

It is true that there are more grey seals on the west coast than common seals. But there are far more grey seals anyway, so numerical generalizations are misleading too. The really important differences between the two British species are that the grey seal congregates often in large numbers in one place to breed, and its pup is stuck on land or in very shallow water for the first month of life (average thirty-two days). The common seal, on the other hand, does not accumulate to breed and the pup takes to the water straightaway. In Shetland common seals are born in the sea.

For ten months of the year adult grey seals disperse all round

Fig. 2 Grey Seal distribution
Known breeding colonies around Britain and Ireland *(Major sites are named)*

North Rona

Orkneys

Monachs
St Kilda

Farnes

Pembroke

our coasts. Tagging experiments from the Farne Islands and other breeding colonies have produced returns from Norway, Iceland, the Faroes, all round Ireland, Brittany, the Netherlands, Denmark, Sweden, West Germany and even Spain. The first grey seal ever tagged, by Mrs Hickling at the Farne Islands in 1951, was a moulter of three to four weeks old which calmly nipped across to Stavanger in Norway within the first fifteen swimming days of its life. While these returns have provided very few answers to the puzzle of grey seal dispersal, they have posed many questions and this work now represents one of the most important facets of grey seal research.

The biggest question of all, of course, is food, and it is still not clear whether these movements over long distances are related to food supply or fish migration. Seals, like any other animal, are capable of getting disorientated, storm-washed or just plain lost, and these relatively long-distance returns cannot reasonably be said to detract from the generalization that grey seals remain in inshore waters for most of their year. Reports from fishermen of seals beyond the continental shelf are rare. On the other hand, as any coastal observer can see for himself, the incidence of seals around those areas of coast we know they like is high – and this is borne out by reports from inshore fishermen.

In general, then, it can be said that the grey seal spends its year among islands and rocky coasts, in estuaries and remote coastal areas where disturbance by man is geographically limited. To breed, it congregates within this habitat in a small number of crowded island colonies and a larger number of isolated cave and remote coastal breeding places where a very few animals may be experimenting to establish new colonies.

LOCOMOTION

In the water the grey seal is a very powerful and graceful swimmer. Anyone who has swum with seals under water experiences a submarine ballet comparable to the elegance of birds in the air, but at a pace better suited to observation by man.

The power-to-weight ratio of an aquatic animal is quite different from that of a land animal. Because the water carries much of the weight of the beast it can afford to be much larger and heavier than would be possible on land. It is most noticeable that whales and sea-lions and sea-cows have utilized the same principle, with the added advantages which all marine mammals have, of being able to withstand great pressure and being insulated from very cold water by a thick and heavy layer of blubber.

In the water the grey seal has to be powerful enough to over-haul fast and agile species of fish like salmon and mackerel, as well as predatory species like conger eels. It is hard to understand how those huge and savage conger eels, up to eight feet in length, are caught. They are so fast and powerful themselves that they would seem to be invincible. But caught they are, as we shall see later in the interview with Sir Frank Fraser Darling, and apparently not infrequently.

This underwater agility in the seal comes from its broad, flattened fore-limbs, which are very strong, and its wide, spade-like rear flippers, which are not so powerful, but which are much more versatile in flexibility and shape, so that they can perform the functions of steering and manoeuvring to a high degree. Cruising seals swim largely with these rear flippers, but the moment a dive or sudden spurt of speed is needed, massive acceleration is produced by leverage against the water from the fore flippers. Both sets of limbs rely greatly upon the seal's cigar-like hydro-dynamic shape, which is as vital a part of the animal's adaption to marine life as are the flipper limbs.

On land, everything is reversed. The seal's weight is a huge disadvantage. The rear flippers are useless and the front limbs have to do all the pulling. Gone, too, is any semblance of grace or agility. The animal becomes an ungainly, cumbrous beast, shuffling about on its belly, unable to reverse or turn quickly, and soon short of breath and energy if it has to travel any distance. Because of all these complications grey seals rarely go very far from the sea. Those on North Rona go furthest because many generations of freedom from interference and predation by man have allowed the colony to spread all over the island, overcrowding forcing the cows further and further uphill and inland to give birth.

Nevertheless it is remarkable how fast a grey seal can move if it panics. By a process of muscular shuffles between thorax and abdomen and very strong forward pulling by the fore flippers, the seal can move over rough rocky terrain faster than a man can run over the same ground. On the occasions when man has been charged by an angry seal on rocky ground, as in the Orkneys in 1848 (see page 31) the seal has the advantage because man is ill-equipped to keep his balance while floundering through weed-strewn boulders and slippery pools. The experiment is not to be recommended. Such aggression is strictly defensive in a situation where the seal knows very well it is extremely vulnerable. In the water, on the other hand, where man is out of his element, grey seals have never been known to attack a swimmer.

FOOD

The practical difficulties involved in following a seal about under water and examining its every mouthful put the operation out of the question, even if, as is doubtful, a seal would feed normally with its arch-predator peering at it through goggles. We can, and have put a seal in a glass-sided tank and fed it a wide variety of food, but this tells us only what a seal *will* eat under very unnatural conditions. For the same reason figures and food lists from zoos and aquaria are only the roughest guide to a wild grey seal's diet. The only way we can be sure of getting accurate results is by killing seals actually feeding and immediately examining their stomach contents, or killing seals which have just hauled out after feeding. But there are logistical problems here. First of all, when you shoot a seal in the water it usually vomits and sinks. And if you catch the seal hauled out, the time lapse between the seal finishing feeding and coming ashore to rest is usually sufficient for the powerful digestive acids to have broken the food down so much that it is not identifiable as anything beyond general fish food. Coupled with this, seals have a habit of eating only the soft flesh of some species, which breaks down very quickly and any-way has no bones or heads to help the poor marine biologist sort it out. (A table showing the contents of the stomachs examined is given in Appendix 5, page 160.)

Even if we overcome these problems by constant and diligent research, who is to say that the seals killed and examined are representative of whole populations and whole age groups, which may be feeding quite differently? Clearly we need years and years of experience of this sort of research, conducted throughout the range of the grey seal and in every month of the year, to discover what and how much the grey seal eats. That will take a long time to get. It is certainly no slight on the endeavours of those scientists who have done the work so far. On the contrary, our existing knowledge is an excellent spring-board from which to make the high dive into the gaping void of un-knowledge.

In conclusion it should be pointed out that almost all scientists, naturalists and fishermen agree that the grey seal is an extremely versatile carnivore which eats from its food types according to their availability. It is also widely agreed that young grey seals probably exist on the stationary members of the diet sheet before learning to catch fish, and that, when in breeding condition, both males and females stop feeding for a while. Territorial bulls may not eat for the entire month or five weeks on shore, whereas peripheral bulls may fast for a much shorter period. Breeding cows do not lose condition as rapidly as bulls, despite lactation, and it is therefore thought that they might feed between lactation and mating, although clearly they do not go very far to sea. Even less is known about non-breeding and immature seals during the same period.

BREEDING

It is the breeding period in the seal's life about which we know most. Apart from the war years, researchers have been able to work on these land-based weeks in the grey seal calendar ever since Fraser Darling first started in the thirties.

Most colonies build up in the autumn or early winter, but on the Pembrokeshire coast pups are born in the spring between March and May. Cows usually arrive at breeding colonies at the same time as the bulls, although they remain quite separate throughout the pupping period. While the cows are giving birth and feeding their pups the bulls are establishing territories near by which the cows will drift into to form harems when they come into oestrus.

A single long white-coated pup is born on or above high-tide line. Very few are born in the water, and they probably perish quickly if they are. They can keep afloat from birth, but little else, and any strong wave or current will quickly dash them against rocks or drown them. Twins are unknown, although twin foetuses have been very occasionally recorded.

Pup mortality is very high in crowded colonies and colonies badly hit by storm. Only 40 per cent of pups born ever reach breeding age. At only a few days old the pup begins to lose its white fur, which is replaced by a short and very beautiful second coat of dappled silver-grey. This is the commercially sought-after coat and, at a month old, just before the pup takes off to sea, it is at its sleekest and best. Many pups are taken both under licence and illegally at this time for their skins.

After birth the cows lactate straightaway, providing the fat necessary for the pup to fill out by putting on an insulatory layer of blubber all over. Seal milk is 35 per cent fat, compared with 3.5 per cent for saleable cow's milk in Britain. This rich milk enables the pup to increase from an average 32 lb. (14 kg) at birth at the rate of 5 lb. (2.3 kg) a day for about sixteen days. Some pups have been seen to suckle after this, but the majority are abandoned by their mothers at this stage. Exactly when this happens depends upon the age and experience of the cow and the onset of postpartum oestrus.

As soon as the cow does begin to come into season she becomes receptive to the attentions of a bull and will leave her pup to take up a place in a territorial bull's harem. These bulls have been arguing about a territory for over a fortnight by this time and are well established. A big bull will command a harem of up to twenty cows. Each cow may be mated several times, often on land but also in the water or in rock pools. The mating itself can be a protracted affair lasting up to an hour, and can be accompanied by much struggling and 'rough' handling, but this probably depends upon the receptibility of the cow. Cows in full season welcome the presence of the bull and mating commences straightaway without any fuss.

Researchers disagree about the replacement of spent bulls and fertilized cows. It seems certain that some replacement does take place, but without any proven system. After a while the territorial bull is either too busy or too tired to see other bulls off, and an incomer may pinch half his cows, forming two harems where previously there was one.

At this point there may be little real fighting between bulls, but earlier on, when they first come ashore, clashes are common and there is much scarring of neck blubber and bleeding.

Alongside these breeding colonies of grey seals may be congregations of immature seals which will not come into breeding condition. Since cows are normally five years old before they are sexually mature, and bulls, although capable at six, are not likely to hold territory until they are ten, it will be seen that there must always be a large number of immature seals attached to any breeding unit. It is possible that virgin cows are impregnated by young (six to nine year) bulls at these adjacent haul-outs, or around the edges of the breeding colonies themselves.

Cows may live to be, and can still be fertile at, thirty-five years, but bulls achieve only twenty years or thereabouts. Age is determined by counting annual cementum layers in canine teeth. There is no reliable method of ageing adult seals in the field.

PREDATORS, PARASITES AND DISEASE

Killer whales do take grey seals from time to time throughout their range, but since these whales are scarce in British waters they are not a significant factor. Man has been the main predator since the ice age. There is a louse and a mite which are parasitic on seals. There is a lungworm, a nematode stomach worm, and a number of other worm types which infest various organs. Diseases recorded mainly relate to bacterial infections on sickly or dying pups. Cancer of the uterus has also been found.

SENSES

Sight is adapted for under-water use and because of this may be poor when the animal is above the surface. Seals will certainly come very close to an unidentified strange object, apparently to get a better 'look'.

Hearing is acute and important. Some researchers have been led to believe that all seals (and many other sea mammals as well) may have better hearing in the upper range than in the lower. This may include sounds which are ultrasonic to man, but this is still uncertain. It must be significant that water is such a good medium for the transmission of sound waves.

Scent clearly works well, too, when the animal is on land, and, although the nostrils close for under-water swimming, the wet nose (like a dog's) remains well supplied with nerves to collect and 'taste' chemical stimuli in the water.

Touch, through the vibrissae whiskers which protrude from the muzzle, is thought to be vitally important. The nerve supply to these whiskers is extensive and clearly of advantage to the seal. These tactile organs probably pick up vibrations in the water which lead to the detection of prey. We know very little about the full use of vibrissae.

Man has always had great difficulty in fully comprehending the extent and potential of sensory organs he does not possess, and the further development of those he does. Our preoccupation with 'extra-sensory' perception relates to these difficulties. However, the naturalist studying any animal with greatly different senses from his own quickly discovers his inadequacies and a glimpse is sometimes gained into the possibilities open to other animals. The cases of blindness in seals – the cause is unknown – are a good example of this. These wild seals, tested to be totally blind, have been seen to be fit and capable in every other way. How do they catch fish? How do they find their way back to their pup? We can only guess at the answers to these mysteries, but cope they do, as well as any sighted seal, which proclaims loudly the limitations of our understanding of seal senses.

RELATIONS WITH MAN

When the ice withdrew from Britain and man migrated north to colonize the springing forests of Scotland and the Isles, he did so up the coast because his culture was that of a shore-line hunter-fisherman. The grey seal was there first to help him with this fresh landscape and for eight thousand years or more seals have been an important source of skins and food and oil. No other mammal has contributed with such versatility to man's progress during those formative years. In many areas a curious relationship sprang up between man and beast. Man drove them to the edge of extinction and then built them into his folklore and legend as mystical, half-human and benign. Conflict is nothing new. In more recent times man has replaced his need of the seal with fossil oil, cloth and agriculture. All that is left is the negative dismissal of the old relationship because of the fish the seal eats.

Salmon fishermen have suffered from the predation of fish from their nets, and, far more infuriating than the loss of a salmon, damage to the nets.

White fish authorities believe that a large population of seals do damage to commercial fish stocks and that the cod-worm, a parasite harmless but unsightly, is spread to the fish by grey seals.

Seal colonies do cause soil and vegetation erosion on some islands where there is overcrowding and they force out plant, bird and insect life which is seen to be equally valuable.

In a few areas like Orkney and the Hebrides seals are an attraction to tourists and visitors, while sealing for pelts is a small and local industry in remote areas around Britain even today and every year licences are granted for pups to be taken for this purpose. Seal shooting for sport has been considered to be an important measure of a hunter's ability in the past, but if it is continued today it can be of little consequence.

All seal literature is punctuated with excuses, conditional clauses and speculation. 'It is estimated that . . .' 'It may be assumed that . . .' 'If these estimates are correct it is clear that . . .' 'If such and such is constant it follows that . . .' and so on. Whereas you can put a radio collar on an elephant and follow it about day and night, watching it feed, mate and die, with a seal this is simply not (yet) possible. It therefore follows that seal research is forced to be much more speculative than many other mammal studies. This is not to imply criticism of the workers or their methods. The whole of science has evolved by a series of hunches later verified by conclusive research. Darwinian theory is the epitome of this. It would be totally negative to suggest that assumptions are not relevant until the facts are known to back them up. The point, surely, is that speculation must not, through familiarity, be taken as fact, especially when used to support an important policy decision.

Back in the days when the study of animals was the naturalist's art, pursued in the field, often at great personal discomfort, it was a relatively simple matter to assess the written workings of any naturalist. As more workers came into the field, a cross-checked body of information accumulated upon which future work could be based. Since the war, however, both in Britain and elsewhere, the work of the naturalist has become more and more technical. Whole new sciences, such as mathematical bioeconomics and statistics, have arisen and conclusions are now reached, not in the field, but in the computerized laboratory. The field naturalist nowadays, as often as not, has to rely on someone else to interpret his own work for him through a series of statistical programmes. Nowhere is this more true than in the field of seal research. It means that the workings of modern animal (and other) studies can no longer be assessed or checked by the amateur. Science has once again removed itself from the common touch.

What alarms the present writer is that the processes of mathematical logic now used are so dynamic, and can project so far into the future, that it must take decades of field research to check them out. And the longer the period of time an assessment of this nature covers, the greater is the number of variables which may be found to have been omitted or unexpected ones which may emerge. It should also be said that the method of modern statistics has, concurrently with its own progression, evolved systems of constantly checking its own findings, and of building in safety factors to allow for human and progressional errors. It follows that these safety measures are also incomprehensible to the amateur.

All seal researchers agree that no one can proceed very much further without a good supply of dead animals. The results which have accrued to us from the various quite extensive culls of Farne Island grey seals in 1972 and 1975 (a total of 2,756 animals, comprising 1,379 adults and 1,377 pups over the two years) have been greatly beneficial to our knowledge, especially the determination of the age structure of a given population and the relevant life-table thus produced. Before this, the Nature Conservancy's Grey Seals Research Officer had to shoot his own specimens, or rely on those provided by salmon netting or zoos. There were sizable gaps in the calendar of dead seal examination because those shot were mostly taken from breeding or moulting haul-outs, and the salmon nets caught seals only when the salmon were running. Records for whole sections of the year were, and still are, missing, because of the dispersal of the animals outside these seasons.

What is needed is a pelagic seal research unit with licence to drift about all over grey seal territory, all the year round, taking adult seals from their various feeding grounds so that a more composite picture of their movements and feeding habits can be built up. This is possibly one area where statistics are slow to assist.

To sum up:

We have a good knowledge of the British grey seal's biology, behaviour and social structure from a few well-studied breeding colonies, notably North Rona, Orkneys and the Farne Islands, but we have very little of this information directly relating to small and peripheral breeding units.

There is very little information available on the feeding habits of grey seals except where they come into direct conflict with man's interests. This information is therefore understandably one-sided.

There is very little information available on either of the other two grey seal populations, the Baltic and the north-western Atlantic. These are currently being studied.

Information on grey seal damage to man's fishing interests is inevitably speculative but has been assessed logically within the parameters of available fact.

CHAPTER 4

Those For and Those Against

To explain all things in nature is too difficult a task for
any one man or even for any one age. 'Tis much
better to do a little with certainty, and leave the rest for
the others that come after you, than to explain all
things.

Isaac Newton, 1713

The 1978 cull controversy is unique in the history of British nature
conservation because of the direct physical confrontation between
the Greenpeace volunteers and their allies and the hired operators
of the cull. Because it made good television and journalism it was,
no doubt as Greenpeace intended, blown up into a headline issue.
Whether or not the cull would have gone ahead without the direct
action on the part of the environmentalist lobby, we shall never
know. It is certainly true that other less forthright organizations
were deeply concerned about the cull, and were making strong representations to the Secretary of State for Scotland to have it
stopped. But it is also true that several direct pleas, for instance
from the Orkney MP Mr Jo Grimond, had been turned down. No
doubt it all helped in the long run, but clearly the risk to human
life brought about by the objectors being present on the islands
concerned was something the Secretary of State could not possibly
permit. His hand was forced.

This chapter endeavours to set out in an unbiased form the
various standpoints of the individuals and bodies concerned in this
issue. Certain aspects of the matter were inadequately covered by
the press reports at the time and it is only fair that the bodies
themselves should be given a place to air their full objections or
support. Where an official statement has been provided it is presented in full.

THE SIX-YEAR CONTROL PLAN

Bearing in mind that the Consultative Committee of the Nature Conservancy had considered that damage to fisheries by grey seals was unsupportable in 1963, and recommended control, the Seals Advisory Committee's advice in 1977 was no surprise. They had watched the Scottish grey seal population grow in Orkney, despite an annual pup cull, to double the size it was in 1963.

As a result they recommended that a dramatic reduction of the Scottish population be brought about by an annual cull of 900 breeding cows and their associated pups and 4,000 moulted pups over each of the six years 1977 to 1982 (see the Scottish Office press notice, 6 July 1978, Appendix 1). This was to take place in the Hebrides and in Orkney, with North Rona in alternate years. The advice was based on an assessment of the amount of commercial fish eaten by grey seals at sea, and, so that this assessment could be constantly checked, the carcases would be scientifically examined to produce a gradually increasing amount of knowledge on food consumption. A breakdown of the simple formula used is as follows:

$\frac{2}{3}$ Total annual food consumption of an average seal $\times$ The total number of seals $=$ The predatory impact on commercial fish supplies each year

This relies on three assumptions:

1. That the total consumption of an average seal has been correctly assessed.
2. That the figure of two-thirds of the total diet comprising commercial species of fish is accurate; and
3. That the population of grey seals is accurately known.

At the time of the recommendations it was calculated from this formula that the amount of commercially valuable fish grey seals in Scottish waters were eating was between 5 and 10 per cent of the total catch landed from Scottish waters. This was considered to be too great. The value of this estimated loss to fisheries was put at over £12 million.

THE SUPPORTERS OF THE CONTROL PLAN

1. *The Sea Mammals Research Unit* of the Natural Environment Research Council is the official scientific research body responsible for studying seals and making recommendations on populations and all aspects of seal biology.

2. *The Seals Advisory Committee* is an inter-departmental committee set up by the Natural Environment Research Council under section 13 of the Act to provide the Secretary of State with scientific advice on seal populations and control.

3. *The Department of Agriculture and Fisheries for Scotland.* This government department runs its own fisheries research programme which has examined the effects of seals on fisheries. DAFS scientists have contributed to the evidence for the control programme. The department is represented on the Seals Advisory Committee.

4. *The Fishermen's Federations of Britain and Scotland* are the allied bodies responsible for the representation of fishermen and the protection of their interests.

5. *The Nature Conservancy Council* is the government body which promotes a national policy for nature conservation, and is represented on the Seals Advisory Committee.

6. *The sealing industry* is unrepresented and operates seasonally in the Hebrides and Orkneys and Shetlands as well as one or two places in England and Wales. This little industry is dependent upon licences being granted for seal killing.

7. *The Scottish Society for the Prevention of Cruelty to Animals* is a public subscription society whose objective is to prevent cruelty by man to animals and to encourage kindness and humanity in their treatment. (The society is a borderline support case in the seal cull issue and is included to clarify its position.)

The first four supporters can be grouped together as one whose joint case is well represented by one of the Natural Environment Research Council's press notices of 16 October 1978 prepared by Dr R. M. Laws and Dr C. F. Summers of the Council's Sea Mammals Research Unit:

(1) In 1977 the Department of Agriculture and Fisheries for Scotland and the Nature Conservancy Council approached NERC for advice on possible strategies for achieving the following objectives:

  (a) to reduce the Scottish Grey seal stock to its mid-1960s level in order to protect fisheries.
  (b) to obtain scientific information upon which long-term management of Scottish Grey seals can be based.
  (c) to safeguard existing pup-hunting interests in Orkney and the Outer Hebrides.

(2) Records of pup production data collected from the principal Grey seal breeding assemblies in Great Britain have shown that, over the period for which reliable statistics are available, stocks not subject to any form of control have been increasing at about 7 per cent annually, i.e., doubling in size about every eleven years. Natural regulation of seal numbers through mortality of young pups, the only density-dependent mechanism which has been observed to operate at current population levels, is unlikely to be significant until all available breeding sites are in use, a situation which may not occur for several generations of Grey seals.

(3) Age analysis from tooth rings of breeding females shot at the Farne Islands in 1972 and 1975 has allowed the evaluation of mortality and pregnancy rates for this discrete population. Using this information in conjunction with the long record of pup-production statistics, it has been possible to calculate total population size for an increasing stock, in contrast to an earlier hypothetical model for static populations, and to investigate the effect of different management strategies on population size and stability.

(4) The widespread increase described above could be halted by a massive increase in pup hunting. However, it can be demonstrated theoretically that a population equilibrium established with a fixed pup quota is unstable and that the stock would be vulnerable to environmental conditions affecting the population. Since there is a six-year time lag between birth and first pup the effect of such changes would not be observed until the hunted age groups started to breed. Fixed-quota pup hunting is, therefore, an undesirable method for reducing stock size.

(5) A large one-off adult cull as a means of reducing stock size is equally undesirable. The population would have to be reduced well below the desired level to take account of subsequent entry of females into the breeding stock and stabilization at the new level would have to be by fixed-quota pup hunting with all its disadvantages.

(6) A method which avoids the undesirable effects of fixed-quota pup hunting and massive adult culls is the removal of a smaller number of adults over a longer period of time, the exact period taken to achieve the new level depending on the proportion of the population removed at each stage. This compromise solution, which may if desired be combined with controlled pup hunting, has the following advantages:

  (a) It is safe because the reduction is in small steps and the stock is never put at risk.
  (b) It is flexible since any shortfall in the number of seals killed in a particular year can be adjusted by increasing the size of the following year's cull or by spreading the reduction over a longer period of time.
  (c) It may be continuously monitored if the cull is divided between different geographical localities so that surveys can be integrated in the programme.

(7) Once at the new level, the stock is best stabilized by smaller-scale adult culls. If the size of these culls is made proportional to the previous year's pup production, a powerful form of density dependence is introduced.

(8) NERC advice, based on SMRU research findings, together with other considerations discussed by the Seals Advisory Committee, was conveyed to the Secretary of State. This advice was that, to meet the objectives given in paragraph 1, a culling programme of the type outlined in 6 (c) above should be implemented for the stock of Grey seals breeding in North Rona, the Outer Hebrides and Orkney. This currently numbers about 50,000 individuals (compared with a mid-1960s population of almost 35,000). Current abundance of Grey seals in the British Isles and the world is about 70,000 and 110,000 respectively.

The support given by the Nature Conservancy Council is qualified very clearly in their own press notice, also of 16 October 1978.

The Nature Conservancy Council has been requested to state its position on the culling of Grey seals in North Scotland.

The primary purpose of the cull is for the protection of commercial fisheries interests in Scottish waters and the case for this, advanced by the Department of Agriculture and Fisheries for Scotland, has been accepted by the Seals Advisory Committee, on which the NCC is represented, and by the Secretary of State for Scotland.

Given this, the NCC is concerned, first, that no action should be taken which puts the future of the Grey Seal population at risk. Secondly the NCC is concerned that the maximum scientific information is obtained from the cull about the biology of Grey Seal populations. Thirdly, the NCC is concerned that further information be obtained on the damage which seals cause to fish stocks in British waters.

To provide information on population dynamics and food requirements of Grey Seals requires culling. A management plan has been prepared by the Sea Mammal Research Unit of NERC. This plan is designed to reduce the population by 15,000 in Scottish waters over six years. It can be adjusted on a year to year basis in the light of experience and this will ensure that the cull does not put the population at risk. Animals taken during the cull will be made available to the Sea Mammal Research Unit.

The Nature Conservancy Council is aware of the considerable concern expressed by conservation bodies, both nationally and internationally, about the cull. More particularly, the NCC has received a copy of the resolution of the General Assembly of the International Union for Conservation of Nature and Natural Resources of 4 October addressed to the Secretary of State for Scotland.

Having these considerations in mind, the NCC believes that:

1. Culling may be necessary in the management of stocks of wild animals, including seals, especially when natural predators are absent and populations increase rapidly;

2. Culling of Grey Seals in the proportions suggested for the present cull, provided that its effects are continuously monitored, should not put the population at risk;

3. Culling of Grey Seals is necessary in obtaining a scientifically based evaluation of damage to fisheries, and in prescribing a management programme for the Grey Seal in Britain;

4. Culling of Grey Seals has been effective for over two decades in their management in other areas of British waters in the interests

of fisheries and of the seals themselves and their breeding habitat. (Commercial culls of pups have also been carried out in Scottish waters.)

Since there is no official voice for the sealing industry, the author has privately approached individuals in current possession of licences to cull seals, for a statement of their support. It can be broadly stated as follows: 'In an area of low employment and low wages we are interested in exploiting this natural resource as has always been done by man. We do it to make money out of the blubber, and the skins which are sold to the luxury leather trade. Since we are dependent upon licences from the government to take pup skins, the only ones of any value to the trade, we must support the cull – although it follows that we want there to be as many seals as possible – as long as we can exploit them.'

There was much confusion about the Scottish Society for the Prevention of Cruelty to Animals' involvement in this controversy. It was incorrectly stated in the press that the Scottish SPCA was supporting the Scottish Office justification for the seal cull. This was not so, and the society is listed here as a borderline supporter only because it took a positive decision to oppose any interference by objectors to the cull on the seal breeding beaches. In a statement issued by Mr G. F. S. Brian, the Society's Secretary, in October 1978 their position is made quite clear:

The Scottish SPCA is not convinced that there is sufficient evidence of damage to domestic fishery stocks to justify a cull, but it is an established fact that the Scottish grey seal population has doubled since the mid-1960s, and this may be partly due to the degree of protection which these animals have had under British law.

The Society's concern is to see that the cull is carried out humanely and that any suffering to orphaned pups is kept to the minimum. With this object it has one Inspector at sea, who will accompany the marksmen, and others on the beaches who will try to ensure after the cull that orphaned pups are killed humanely as quickly as they can be identified.

It would be ironic and very sad if those who disagree so strongly with the cull, presumably on humanitarian grounds for the species is not in danger of extinction, were to be responsible for much unnecessary suffering.

THE OPPOSERS OF THE CONTROL PLAN

1. *The Greenpeace Foundation* is an international group dedicated to non-violent direct action to help solve some of the world's critical environmental problems.

2. *The World Wildlife Fund* is a worldwide fund-raising organization established to help save the world's endangered wildlife.

3. *The International Union for Conservation of Nature and Natural Resources* is an international watchdog organization which concerns itself with all conservation issues anywhere in the world.

4. *The Society for the Promotion of Nature Conservation* is one of the earliest British conservational movements and since 1958 has been the national association of the forty regional Nature Conservation Trusts.

5. *The Scottish Wildlife Trust* is a voluntary membership body limited by guarantee and is dedicated to serving the interests of wildlife in Scotland. Through branches and members' groups the Trust keeps constant surveillance over threatened habitats, and is energetic in the promotion of conservation.

6. *The Fauna Preservation Society*, is a charity dedicated to the protection of endangered animals throughout the world.

7. *The Orkney Field Club* is a membership organization in the Orkney Islands which serves the interests of natural history and field studies for its members. In this case the club members formed an action group called 'Selkie', the Orkney word for seal, to oppose the six-year plan.

8. *The general public* in Britain, which put enormous pressure on the government to stop the cull by writing to the press, the Prime Minister and the Secretary of State for Scotland. Over twenty thousand letters were received about the issue and opinion polls taken in the streets revealed widespread opposition.

Greenpeace UK Ltd issued their own policy statement in October 1978:

Greenpeace is opposed to the grey seal management programme announced by the Department of Agriculture and Fisheries for Scotland (DAFS). The plan envisages killing 900 breeding females and their associated pups plus 4,000 moulted pups each year until 1982, the aim being to reduce the grey seal population in British waters by one half. As two thirds of the world's grey seal population inhabit UK waters, the global grey seal population would be reduced by one third under the plan.

The justification given for this ill-conceived programme is the conservation and protection of fisheries, specifically, (1) damage to salmon fisheries, (2) damage to fish by parasites and (3) damage to fish stocks. The head of the DAFS Marine Laboratory, Basil Parrish, has stated that no link can be established between the increase in the grey seal population and the first two of these categories. Damage to salmon and nets does occur but the incidence of damage has not increased in proportion to the expanding grey seal population. In fact, a switch from natural fibres to synthetic fibres used in net construction has led to a decrease in damage to salmon nets on the Scottish east coast. The most significant damage to the salmon fishery is caused by drift netting operations carried out near Greenland. Drift netting is illegal in Scottish waters, but still continues.

Proponents of the management scheme claim that the seal population in UK waters consume 130,000 tons of fish a year, of which 50 per cent they claim is a loss in the potential annual fishery catch. This estimate is based on a number of assumptions which are not based on any established scientific fact. Neither the quantities of specific fish species consumed by grey seals, nor the feeding habits of grey seals have been adequately assessed. Grey seals are thought to feed intermittently, and not every day, as DAFS has assumed. While on the breeding grounds in the Orkneys or in west Scotland, the seals eat little or no fish, though the length of this fast is undetermined.

Greenpeace views the seal kill as an attempt to shift the blame for declining fish stocks from human over-fishing to the seals. Man has been, and continues to be, the cause in the decline of fish stocks in UK waters. The catch of fish by all vessels in UK waters has increased from 270,866 tons in 1960 to 442,261 tons in 1976. It is also clear that more effort is spent to catch the same unit of fish which further indicates depletion of the fish stocks. It is also because of the increased effort to catch the same unit of fish that prices of fish available to the public has increased.

Greenpeace demands that the 1978 seal kill be suspended and that a full public inquiry be called to examine all aspects of the proposed seal kill. Greenpeace will send a volunteer crew aboard the *Rainbow Warrior* to the seal hunt area to attempt to stop the Norwegian hunters which have been contracted to kill the adult grey seals.

The World Wildlife Fund, the International Union for the Conservation of Nature and Natural Resources, the Society for the Promotion of Nature Conservation, the Scottish Wildlife Trust and the Fauna Preservation Society can be grouped together in opposition. All these organizations challenged the scientific justification for the six-year plan. Some gave money for the Greenpeace direct action in the Orkneys and countered the proposals by advertising for public opposition, and others, like the Scottish Wildlife Trust, sought direct audience with the Secretary of State for Scotland to present corporate opposition and to ask for a moratorium while re-assessment took place.

On 16 October 1978, in Ashkhabad in the USSR, at a meeting of the International Union for Conservation of Nature and Natural Resources, a resolution was passed to send the following cable to the Scottish Office. The contents of this cable serve to illustrate the collective opinions and policies of the independent conservation bodies, representatives of several of which were present in Ashkhabad:

RECOGNIZING that the wildlife management practices of the Government of the United Kingdom have enabled the British population of Grey seals so to increase that it now comprises half of the world population of this species;
RECOGNIZING FURTHER that this is one of the world's rarer seals, and one that has been depleted in many parts of its range outside the UK;
AWARE that inshore fisheries in Scotland have declined in recent years, and that seal numbers have been blamed for adversely affecting commercial fisheries;
CONVINCED that the decline in inshore fisheries is in part due to commercial overfishing;
CONCERNED that the UK Government is planning to reduce Grey seal numbers in Scotland by 50 per cent over the next six years, a cull that it proposes to start during October 1978;

The General Assembly of IUCN, at its 14th Session, Ashkhabad, USSR, 26 September–5 October 1978:

URGES the Government of the United Kingdom to suspend any cull of Grey seals in Orkney, North Rona, and the Western Isles until adequate data on the impact of Grey seals on fish stocks and the role of Grey seals in their ecosystems are available;

RECOMMENDS that stronger conservation measures be introduced to prevent further overfishing of the inshore fish stocks in British waters; and

REQUESTS that a copy of the management plan which prescribes the present cull may be supplied to IUCN for evaluation.

Most important in this case was the backing of the public. Even a very superficial opinion research investigation has shown that, put to a referendum, the public in Britain wanted the cull to be called off. The same investigation revealed that a huge majority did not know why they wanted it stopped or any of the arguments for or against it. They were swayed entirely by emotive arguments on television and in the popular press which almost all obscured any logic on either side. Even those who felt moved enough to write to the press, sign petitions, or appear on television or radio programmes produced high marks for confused and woolly thinking.

While public opinion must be listed as an active force of opposition in the case it is not fair to suggest that it either represents or can be allied to the motives of the other conservation groups. It is hoped that their juxtaposition in reality and in this book serves only to illustrate how powerful the manipulation of public opinion is and how important is the scientific and non-scientific logic employed for it.

Finally the Orkney Field Club and the action group 'Selkie' are worthy of separate mention because they have one objection shared by none of the others. While they support the doubts broadly expressed in the IUCN resolution cabled to the Secretary of State for Scotland, their petition of opposition collected a very large number of signatures from the Orkney population, and illustrated that there was a strong local objection to the seal cull being carried out at all, and in particular in and around the Orkney Islands. It is also significant that some of those who willingly signed the petition were Orkney fishermen who should, apparently, have been in favour of a move which was designed to protect their livelihood. Locally, however, because it is known that grey seals eat squid which in turn prey on lobsters, the lobster fishermen have a tradition that the presence of seals is good for fishing.

Other animal welfare groups and conservation bodies (e.g., the Royal Society for the Prevention of Cruelty to Animals and the Council for Nature) gave their support to the opposition lobby, but, because of the already existing confusion between the SPCAs and because none of the other bodies produced opposition of a new or different nature, it has been decided to keep this list short and strictly related to the action, direct or political, demonstrated during the October 1978 crisis.

CHAPTER 5

The Fishermen's Case

The Fishing Industry is . . . suffering very painfully, in
both human and economic terms, from the imposition
of catch controls throughout all the areas in which it
has traditionally operated.

British Fishing Federation Ltd and
British Fishermen's Federation,
press release, September 1978

Nobody wants to do away with all the seals. We want
just to keep them to a reasonable number.

Mr Alfred Cross,
Chief Fishery Officer for Northumberland,
Daily Telegraph, 13 February 1978

Some of the parameters involved are very difficult to
investigate by direct observation but in the absence
of more rigorous data it is reassuring that several
independently determined evaluations of the impact of
seals on fish stocks by workers in different countries
are in such close agreement.

Dr Charles Summers,
Officer-in-Charge,
Sea Mammals Research Unit,
New Scientist, 30 November 1978

On a boisterous, windy October day I stood on the slippery quay
at Mallaig, the tiny West Highland fishing port, among a dozen
or more inshore trawlers unloading their catch in the noisy and
slimy way that can be observed at any busy fishing port. Mallaig
was busy that day because the herring fleet were making the best
of the summer migration of mackerel into Hebridean waters. But
Mallaig is not a mackerel fishing port; its fortunes have always
swum with the herring, the 'silver darling' which enabled this little
town to grow and prosper like so many others around Scotland's

coast. These boats are unloading mackerel because there is a ban on herring imposed by the government as a conservation measure necessary because of overfishing by British fishermen as well as those of a dozen other nations fishing our common stocks.

Not only is there a ban on herring, but for several years now European fishing fleets have been fishing not to capacity, but to a quota, a further conservation measure because our international stocks of most commercial species are in a bad way. It is widely rumoured in the industry that there is worse to come. Not only is there no end in sight to the herring ban, but fisheries' scientists are said to be advising the governments of the EEC countries that catches should be reduced by a further 25 per cent next year. The industry is worried, and the Associations, who have the job of looking after the interests of fishermen and the industry, are well aware of the problems ahead.

It is hardly surprising that in this climate of uncertainty and cut-back, the Fishermen's Associations should be looking, now more than ever, for ways of alleviating the pressure on the fish stocks without imposing further restrictions on the boats themselves. The Department of Agriculture and Fisheries is concerned in the same way, and for many years government and independent fisheries' scientists have been monitoring the rise and fall of stocks, catches and competition. Seals, dolphins, porpoises and sea-birds have all come in for scrutiny and a considerable scientific literature has accumulated over the years on these problems.

The one competitive factor which has not remained static is the grey seal. Common seals, some cetaceans and some bird species have all become fewer, some considerably and some only a little, but the grey seal has grown from relative scarcity to striking strength. Its population has more than doubled in the past decade and there is every indication that the same will happen again. The reasons for the increase are perfectly clear. Conservation laws, the replacement of seal-oil by paraffin and, most significant of all, the loss of human population from small inclement islands have all allowed the grey seal to come back with a vengeance.

Since none of the factors which used to keep grey seals down in numbers are operative today, and since there is this clear conflict over fish stocks, it seems logical to replace that age-old human predation by a conservation management plan which will, at the same time, both ensure a healthy population of seals and reduce the fishing conflict. It certainly does not seem unreasonable that this should be the line the fisheries' authorities have sought to adopt.

Seen through the fishermen's eyes, if something positive is not done soon, the increasing seal population will make bigger and bigger demands on the fish stocks in order to support its expansion, the conservation efforts of the fishing industry will be impaired by the increased predation, and the conservation measures will continue to force the catches downwards. In order to supply our domestic needs Britain will have to import more fish, which because it has to be paid for in foreign currency, makes it much more expensive. Imports have an adverse effect on the balance of payments and the prices of fish in the shops will have to rise. Housewives will stop buying fish because it is too expensive and the industry will go into decline. Fishing vessels will have to be laid up and the fishermen have to resort to the dole. Again there will be higher costs to the nation in return for no product. Many inshore fishing vessels are partly financed by public money in the form of grants and loans, and, if they fail, the cost to the taxpayer is heavy. And at the end of the day, in the case of Scotland, where many small communities are entirely dependent upon fishing, there is the prospect of complete unemployment and a local slump, with all its concomitant social problems. Back on the quay at Mallaig, with the herring already banned and the mackerel only a seasonal catch, the fears of many of these swarthy, oil-skinned men, as they laugh and shout through the wind and the rain and the omnipresent stench of rotting fish, are all too easy to understand.

But it is very hard to explain to the man in the street that there is a shortage of fish in the sea. It is like telling him that the government is short of money. He doesn't really believe it. As we have seen, Greenpeace point out that the catch in UK waters increased from 270,866 tons of fish in 1960 to 442,261 tons in 1976, largely as a result of smart modern methods and equipment. It is not altogether surprising that there is a herring ban and catch quotas are needed. The seals can hardly be blamed for that. Clearly, the facts need putting before the man in the street very firmly and a common policy of restraint needs to be practised all round, not just by our fishermen, but by all the other countries who fish our waters, seal protection organizations and, by no means least, seals themselves. No one would tolerate an exploding rat or rabbit population in a time of grain shortage, and it is irrational to oppose all seal control in the same way. It remains to the Fishermen's Associations' credit that they have not reacted, as the public did in October 1978, emotionally and subjectively to what must appear to them to be a sharp slap in the face with their own fish.

The impetus to effect seal controls is not new. The Fishing Federations and in particular the Salmon Fishing Authorities have a long record of complaint and parliamentary lobby. Until fairly recently it was the salmon netting industry which was hardest hit. A seal taking salmon from a net not only ate that salmon, but, as often as not, badly damaged the net and let all the other salmon go as well – not an easy situation for anyone employed to catch salmon to accept calmly, especially with a season of a limited number of catching days. Shooting and poison were both used, but a seal head in choppy water is a very difficult target and poison baiting was a laborious nuisance with, in the case of strychnine, an uncomfortable element of risk. Neither method was really effective.

Synthetic fibres have proved to be the answer for the salmon fishermen. Now that the nets are much stronger the seal can no longer do such widespread damage and the poaching of a salmon from the net can be viewed as a supportable natural hazard of the industry. Because of this, and because of the recent increase in the numbers of salmon running into our rivers, the salmon fishing industry has relatively little cause to clamour for grey seal control at the moment. But this situation depends upon there being no serious rise in the numbers of seals found to be stealing from nets or exploiting the salmon runs. There is always the sneaking feeling that if seal numbers get too great and other fish species in its diet continue to become more and more scarce, the salmon could come in for a much larger share of predation than they are receiving at the moment. Besides, the salmon fishing industry, like the white fish industry, has other man-induced worries. If the drift netting of our Atlantic salmon continues to take place, outside our control, off the Greenland coasts and illegally in Scottish waters, during the marine stage of the fish's life cycle and before it has had a chance to return to our rivers to breed, it may be not so very long before the traditional salmon fishing and sporting industries will need every salmon they can catch.

At the instigation of grumbling salmon fishermen as far back as the immediate post-war period, the government set up various committees and research groups to study and monitor the effects of seals on fisheries. Over the years and with the various different seal conservation laws the names and authorities have changed, but the task has remained the same and we do now possess the results of some thirty-five years of investigation and research. There are still huge gaps, but we know from the 1963 Report of the Consultative Committee on Grey Seals and Fisheries that there was then considered to be sufficient evidence and sufficient seals to warrant a control and management programme. (See Appendix 3 for their recommendations.)

Since then, of course, the salmon problem has somewhat alleviated, but through the thirty-five years of research it has become apparent that, salmon quite apart, grey seals must be consuming huge quantities of other fish. Investigations into this have produced the log of scientific data we possess today. Over eight hundred stomachs have been analysed (see Appendix 4) in Scottish waters alone between the years 1958 and 1978, and the evidence from these samples is quite clear. At certain times and in certain places grey seals are eating a high proportion of commercially valuable fish.

Only in recent years, when the need for fish stock conservation has been pressing, has the white fishing industry taken over the grey seal control lobby. In response to renewed pressures scientists sat down to estimate and compute the actual levels of damage to the industry. The results were horrifying. So were the claims. It is unfortunate that the results of these investigations were not co-ordinated from the beginning into one acceptable estimate of damage, because out of the confusion of claim and counter-claim by scientific, political and administrative authorities, much of the concern for the resultant control plan and the call for its rejection have arisen.

In a prominent article in the *Daily Telegraph* in February 1978 the Sea Fisheries Committee in Newcastle-upon-Tyne are reported to be claiming that grey seals eat four to five stone (56–70 lb.) of fish a day, which represents a loss to the fishing industry of £25 million a year. As Mr J. D. R. Bradbeer, clerk to the Northumberland Sea Fisheries Committee, says, this is a fantastic sum. Certainly an element of fantasy is revealed when one looks at the work of Dr B. B. Rae, who produces the average figure of some 15 lb. of fish a day.

Because of this sort of unnecessary confusion, concerning not only feeding estimates but also seal numbers and increase forecasts, I believe the hard core of responsible scientific researchers have been unreasonably challenged and brought into public pillory. It has led to criticisms of the scientific basis for the control plan which speak of guestimates and broad assumptions. The criticisms themselves are, in my opinion, broad assumptions, because the instant experts involved have not even taken the trouble to examine the sources of the evidence for themselves. There is nothing very scientific about that approach. The commonest shuttlecock in the present row is the amount of food a seal eats each day. At one point it was rumoured that the scientists who produced the common standard of 15 lb. of fish a day for all grey seals had phoned a zoo for information on which to base their paper. This sort of ignorant idea is so far from the truth and so unfair as to be virtually slanderous.

The work began in 1960 with Dr Rae, who first produced the figure of 15 lb. per day. This figure was based on unpublished work done by Steven on feeding captive seals, for the very straightforward reason that there was no other information available at that time. In 1968 M. C. Keyes published a work in America which examined several pinneped species and found that there was a daily food requirement of between 6 and 10 per cent of each seal's total body weight. In 1969 D. E. Sergeant published a paper on porpoises which happen to have approximately the same body weight as grey seals. The Keyes principle worked for them too.

Checked against the energy requirements of marine mammals for metabolism and growth, the 6–10 per cent rule is seen to be adequate, but likely to be an underestimation. Much more recently Summers, Bonner and Haaften in 1978 used a daily grey seal feeding rate of 22 lb. for a period of 300 days in the year to make allowance for the periods of fast during moulting and breeding. This works out at 18 lb. per day on a 365-day basis. The 15 lb. quota is still seen to be on the safe side.

In their important paper in 1977 (reproduced in Appendix 4), Basil Parrish, Director of the Marine Laboratory of the Department of Agriculture and Fisheries in Aberdeen, and his colleague from the Freshwater Fisheries Laboratory in Pitlochry, W. M. Shearer, accepted the 15 lb. quota on the above values and applied it to the average seal weight, to arrive at an average daily feeding rate in the total seal population. The weights used, as supplied by the Sea Mammals Research Unit, whose job it is to collect and tabulate such essential data, are:

> Immatures 100 kg for 60 per cent of the population
> Adults ♀   150 kg ⎫
>   ♂   200 kg ⎬ for 40 per cent of the population

This gives a conservative overall weighted average for the whole population of 120 kg or 264 lb., and 6–10 per cent body weight gives a conservative average daily feeding rate of between 15 and 25 lb. Again, the 15 lb. quota can be seen to be an acceptable standard. Any suggestion that this is not a logical progression based on all the scientific data available is fallacious, and it is even more extreme to demand that a comprehensive study of food consumption rates of grey seals in the wild should be made before any estimates of total consumption can be accepted. The distribution of the animals outside the breeding season is so wide and so diverse that any representative study by observation is currently impossible. In addition, the extremely rapid digestion of food in the seal stomach, and the common occurrence of vomiting on being shot or caught, makes the data available from stomach analysis slow to accumulate and unreliable.

In response to these criticisms and demands, Dr Charles Summers, Officer-in-Charge of the Sea Mammals Research Unit, expressed his own opinions in an article in the *New Scientist* in November 1978.

Much more disturbing was the reaction to, and statements made about, the cull by a number of apparently reputable national and international conservation and animal welfare organizations. It is to be expected that such organizations would wish to have a policy towards wildlife management issues. But when authoritative sounding spokesmen attack the scientific basis of such an issue, without presenting evidence upon which to base constructive alternatives, on behalf of societies which themselves have no record of relevant expertise, they cannot fail to damage the image of the conservation movement at large.

Dr Summers's article goes on to defend the management plan and he adds support to the British policy by spreading the scientific base to include work done by Canadian, Icelandic and Scandinavian scientists, many of whom have accepted the same values and standards for assessing the impact of grey seals on fish stocks, and whose independent results are reassuringly comparable. But he returns to the more far-reaching issue of conflict:

But whatever fine tuning is applied to the data [by independent assessments] it remains irrefutable that grey seals are becoming more abundant throughout most of their range and that they have an impact on fisheries that is quantifiable within limits. The fact that overfishing, restrictive fisheries legislation and foreign trawlers have a greater impact than the seals on fish stocks, or that sea-birds and cetaceans also eat fish, does not make the uncontrolled expansion of grey seal stocks acceptable to the British fishing industry.

Even if, by exerting responsible political pressure, society chooses to accept this loss from the fishery in order to preserve seals for posterity there remain good biological reasons for doing this by positive management. The notion that if man allows nature to take its own course everything will be all right, which in this instance has been identified by some organizations as the conservation objective, is a naive and unscientific concept.

The article closes on a distinctly chilly and uncompromising note which perhaps illustrates that in some quarters the damage to the conservation movement at large which Dr Summers mentions above has already begun:

Because of the recent action of protest groups, which was sensationalized by the media, trial of wildlife management policy by public opinion, however manipulated or ill-informed, is now a force to be reckoned with. When the animal welfare and conservation groups flex their political muscle in order to shape that opinion, it is to be hoped that they will make a genuine effort to sustain credibility at any proper scientific forum in which they may participate.

It remains to be seen what the outcome of independent assessments will be, but it is certain that no new facts will become available in the short term. A characteristic of seal research has been the slow and even torturous accumulation of data. Any resentment felt by the scientific faction at what has been described as amateur and idealistic intervention must be at least partly justified.

There is little that can be said about the cod-worm hazard. There is no doubt that this parasite is spread by grey seals and that as long as there are seals there will always be cod-worm in a proportion of the fish we catch. Since no one has ever suggested doing away with all the seals in the North Atlantic, some measure of this nuisance to the fishing industry must be an entirely acceptable natural hazard, just as bad weather is a nuisance to the catching process. What worries the industry at the moment is the level of infestation of the cod coming ashore. It appears to be static at the moment despite the rise in seal numbers, but the concern is that a large increase will be recorded after several years of uncontrolled increase in the final host. The knowledge that in the past whole Norwegian fishing towns and villages went out of business because severe infestations of the worm made the preparation of the fish too costly an exercise is an often quoted bit of history and it must be near the surface of the argument behind the fisheries' case.

At the time of writing the fishing industry in Britain is in a curious state of flux. Mr John Silkin has the unenviable task of fighting for an acceptable catch quota from EEC common fish stocks. Conservation controls and bad relations with the other fishing nations are already against him. Recently, however, a new twist to the seal problem has threatened to make Mr Silkin's job even harder.

It has been suggested by a Stonehaven fisherman, Mr Ian Macdonald, both on television and in a written paper, that the fisheries' scientists who prepared the estimates of damage to fish stocks are wildly underestimating the actual situation. Mr Macdonald has taken it upon himself to become a spokesman for his industry and he is apparently determined to present the fisheries case for a grey seal cull with as much vigour as it was opposed by the environmentalists. Accepting the figure of 15 lb. of fish a day for the average grey seal and the generally agreed British (1977) population total of 69,000 animals, his paper presents these new calculations.

The most recent published population figure is 69,000 seals. Assuming that some of these are immature and not wishing to be accused of being unfair to the seals, we will only use the figure of 60,000 in our calculations. Each seal must eat 15 lb. of fish daily to sustain itself.

Daily consumption by 60,000 seals @ 15 lb. = 402 tons of fish.

Annual consumption 60,000 × 15 × 365 = 146,651 tons of fish.

To be fair to the seals we have to admit that the international scientists advise that only some 85–86 per cent of the grey seal's diet comes from the species of fish of importance commercially to man. To further favour the seals we will only use a figure of 80 per cent.

Therefore the annual consumption of fish of value to man, 80 per cent of 146,651 = 117,321 tons. This is the amount of fish that the seals must actually eat to keep alive but unfortunately for man and our fish stocks, seals are top carnivores, efficient killers and highly selective feeders. They prefer the largest fish available and feed only on particular choice parts of the fish, notably the livers and roes. This selective diet results in the destruction of a far greater weight of fish than is actually eaten. The actual factor by which we must multiply our fish consumption figure is open to dispute with varying scientific opinions, ranging from four to seven times. To be least damaging to the seals case, we have used the lowest factor proposed. This means that the seals must destroy fish weighing some 469,286 tons, in order to satisfy their known food requirement. This enormous figure is remarkably similar to the total catch by all British boats from home waters last year, and also very close to the total allowable catch by international quota from these waters by the British fleet.

Against this massive allegation the Parrish and Shearer estimate of 65,000 tons looks very reasonable.

Mr Macdonald's hypothesis is not a scientific work and does not purport to be. It is the heartfelt speculation of a directly involved participant who feels that it is better for fish stocks and their management as a food resource to overestimate any threat to it in just the same way as many of the conservationist and environmentalist faction have tried to reduce the very conservative scientific estimates on which the cull programme was based. Mr Macdonald may be wrong, but there is an uncomfortable ring of truth about his down-to-business logic. Certainly the Fishermen's Federations think so, as do many of his fellow fishermen, and, as he himself warns, European governments have already found it advantageous to accept his arguments, at least in part, and to look on these fish as a second quota being taken by Britain from EEC common fish stocks. He correctly points out that no other nation is asking for two quotas, and no other nation is wilfully protecting a major hazard to food production. This is an unfortunate standard for Mr Silkin to have to carry into battle. Nor is a popular argument of this severity going to make the true job of conservation of seals any easier. Could it be that Greenpeace and its supporters have stirred up a hornet's nest which will end up by stinging everyone in the eye, including the seals, before it settles again? Dr Summers's plea for 'credibility in any proper scientific forum' will have been a lone voice in the wilderness indeed if politicians in Europe choose to accept even part of these fishermen's claims. Politicians are not known for scientific argument. Like Mallaig, Stonehaven is a small fishing community, and, like Mallaig, it has felt the constrictions of catch controls and the herring ban. If it was a farming community and Mr Macdonald was estimating a loss of cereal to an expanding rat population his figures would not even be checked, let alone challenged. But seals, we all know, are different, and Mr Macdonald and the rest of his industry must, apparently, accept that the difference is a rational one. Somebody once said that irrationally held truths may be better than reasoned errors. If that is to be the case in this issue, someone must do some quick and skilful preaching to our fishermen.

CHAPTER 6

The Interviews

Twelve questions covering the main points at issue in the seal cull controversy were put by the author to seven people representing a cross-section of opinion. These personal interviews all took place after the grey seal cull was called off. The opinions expressed here are personal, regardless of the individual's employment or affinity with any party or organization. Several of the interviewees serve currently on the advisory councils of various scientific bodies, government departments and other important organizations. The purpose here of listing such appointments in a biographical introduction is to enable the reader to see what level of experience and achievement the opinion is based on, not to suggest that the views of those organizations are represented.

In some respects it would have been easier to adopt the usual journalistic method of approaching the corporate bodies in conflict and putting questions to a spokesman from each, but it is often the case that some internal political situation, nothing to do with the issue in question and quite invisible to the outside world, prevents a spokesman from giving his own opinion, which may actually be more relevant than the official one. A good example of this occurred recently when an excellent scientist told the author that, although he personally saw no reason why the control programme should not be carried out, the organization he worked for had decided to oppose it because they felt it was a good principle to question any government policy.

Of course, there is no guarantee that the opinions independently expressed are any more rational or uninhibited, but, by a careful selection process, and by discussing the whole controversy personally with each interviewee, it is hoped that straightforward informed opinion has been achieved. Most importantly, it is not the object of these interviews to examine the scientific (or any other) basis of the cull proposals. This has been done in detail elsewhere in the book; rather it is to help the reader to make up his own mind from this encounter with very experienced and involved people.

The questions were put to the following:

1. *An international ecologist* Sir Frank Fraser Darling, D Sc, L L D, F R S E, is chosen because he is a pioneer ecologist of world renown. He is a Vice-President of the Conservation Foundation in the U S A, as well as serving on many bodies in the U K, among them the Nature Conservancy, the Scottish Wildlife Trust and the International Union for Nature Conservation. His Reith Lectures, 'Wilderness and Plenty', set the scene for European Conservation Year 1969, and they have contributed strikingly to the impact of the conservation movement on world opinion. He is the author of many books, particularly on Scotland, is a pioneer student of Hebridean grey seals, and has spent a lifetime studying the relationship of man to his environment all over the globe.

2. *An international conservationist* Sir Peter Scott, C B E, D S C, is Chairman of the World Wildlife Fund (International), Chairman of the Survival Service Commission of the International Union for Conservation of Nature and Natural Resources, Chairman of the Fauna Preservation Society and Honorary Director of the Wildfowl Trust. Since the Second World War he has been involved closely with conservation on international, national and local scales, and has developed the reserves of the Wildfowl Trust which are involved in showing waterbirds to the public. He was architect of I U C N's Red Data Books; principal rescuer of the Hawaiian Goose and several other species of wildfowl from extinction; promoter of conservation education on television and in the field; painter and writer; and recipient of the U N Environment Prize.

3. *An international seal biologist* W. Nigel Bonner, B Sc, is one of Britain's leading seal researchers. He is the author of many scientific papers contributing to our knowledge of seals, and the co-author of the existing management plan now in use on Farne Island grey seals. He was formerly head of the Seals Research Division of the Institute for Marine Environmental Research, and is currently serving the British Antarctic Survey as head of Life Sciences. Nigel Bonner has studied Antarctic fur seals, elephant seals, leopard seals, weddell seals and crab-eater seals in the

southern hemisphere as well as having been associated with scientific observation of the whaling industry in South Georgia since 1953. He is a marine mammalologist of global experience as well as an authority on British seals.

4. *A pioneer British seal researcher* Mrs Grace Hickling, MBE, MA, is the Honorary Secretary of the Natural History Society of Northumbria, a member of the Farne Islands local committee, and a Vice-Chairman of the Council for Nature. She is the author of *Grey Seals and the Farne Islands*, an important milestone in seal literature, and is a veteran of grey seal research. She was the first scientist to tag and record the return of a grey seal from overseas and she has dedicated her working life to the Farne Island grey seals since 1951.

5. *A direct-action environmentalist* Mr Alan Thornton is a director of the Greenpeace Foundation. He has worked with Greenpeace for three years both in Canada, where he was working on the harp seal exploitation conflict, and latterly in Britain. He is particularly interested in sea mammals and the contamination of the world's oceans through industrial pollution. He has contributed articles to relevant periodicals on both sides of the Atlantic.

6. *A government fisheries scientist* Mr Basil B. Parrish, BSc, FRSE, FIBiol, is the Director of Fisheries Research in the Department of Agriculture and Fisheries for Scotland. He is the author of numerous scientific papers on, and has contributed substantially to our knowledge of, the biology, ecology and conservation of exploited fish resources in the north-east Atlantic. He is currently President of ICES, a Council member of the Scottish Marine Biological Association, and has served as President of the (now defunct) Aberdeen and North of Scotland Zoological Society. Mr Parrish has been interested in and involved with grey seals for ten years.

7. *A naturalist in Parliament* The Right Honourable Earl of Cranbrook, CBE, Hon. MA (Cantab), is widely known for his dedication to wildlife and conservation. Since 1970 he has been Chairman of the Seals Advisory Committee and his other appointments include the Council of the Nature Conservancy 1967, the Council of London Zoo, a Trustee of the British Museum of Natural History, Treasurer to the Linnean Society 1958, Treasurer

of the University of East Anglia 1964, and a member of the Standing Commission on Museums and Galleries from 1965. He was responsible in Parliament for the Animal Cruel Poisons Act 1963, the Conservation of Seals Act 1970, and the Conservation of Wild Creatures and Wild Plants Act 1975. He has been a naturalist all his life, but, he insists, not a scientist. He is a bird watcher, not an ornithologist, and a seal watcher, not a researcher. Lord Cranbrook figures very prominently in the grey seal controversy.

Question 1.   *Have you ever seen a grey seal?*

Sir Frank Fraser Darling: Yes, I have lived alone with grey seals on North Rona and the Treshnish Isles for weeks at a time.

Sir Peter Scott: Yes, I've seen lots. I've seen them on the Farne Islands; I've seen them in West Wales; and I've swum with them under water in Iceland. So I do know grey seals rather well.

Mr W. Nigel Bonner: Yes, very many times. I first watched grey seals over thirty years ago in Cornwall, and I started an intensive study of British grey seals in 1967.

Mrs Grace Hickling: Yes. I have worked with grey seals for nearly thirty years.

Mr Alan Thornton: Yes. I have seen them in the Orkneys and also in captivity.

Mr Basil B. Parrish: Yes, both in the field and also in captivity. My association with seals in the field has been as a genuine lover of them, but also in relation to my professional duties as a fisheries scientist.

The Earl of Cranbrook: I have been a naturalist and conservationist all my life; I must have watched hundreds of grey seals.

Question 2.   *Do you think that because seals are thought to be intelligent mammals they should be treated differently from other, lower animals which conflict with man's interests?*

Sir Frank Fraser Darling: No, because they still have the same biological capacity for inordinate increase which any other animal has.

Sir Peter Scott: It's very hard to say whether they should be treated any differently. I think all animals have certain rights to being properly treated by man, but on the other hand perhaps one does tend to think in terms of the more intelligent ones being given more consideration.

Mr W. Nigel Bonner: I don't think intelligence really comes into it because it is so difficult to define. But I do think that more consideration should be given to the treatment of a seal than to a liver fluke, for example, but not necessarily more than to the treatment of a rat.

Mrs Grace Hickling: I wouldn't think so, no.

Mr Alan Thornton: No. From a conservation point of view I think it is very important to ensure the survival of *all* species.

Mr Basil B. Parrish: No. I don't think that because they are 'higher' animals they should receive any different treatment from lower ones in the context of their management in relation to man's interests.

The Earl of Cranbrook: Well, I don't think that there are any mammals that I've ever met which are less intelligent than seals. I would readily agree that you've got to be much more careful of any prospect of inflicting cruelty on a mammal than you have on an insect but I don't think any mammals suffer less pain than others. I wouldn't differentiate seals from any other mammal.

Question 3 *What effect has the recent publicity had on your opinion of the proposed control measures?*

Sir Frank Fraser Darling: I am rather aghast at it in its failure to see the problems and the possible ways out of it. The population of grey seals in Great Britain is very much larger than it was a few years ago, but if we look back in history, sea boots were made of seal skin. Now they are made of rubber. There has been a terrific let-up or amelioration of killing seals within the last hundred years and the result has been an increase. They are a species which can multiply fairly quickly because they live a long time, so that you can get a large increase within a fairly few years and this has occurred in the British Isles.

Sir Peter Scott: Well, not really any, largely because I wasn't in Britain during most of it. I was at a conference of the International Union for Conservation of Nature and Natural Resources in USSR, where indeed we were discussing the grey seal situation without the influence of British press publicity.

Mr W. Nigel Bonner: I think the proposed control measures were soundly based to start with, and none of the publicity I've seen has made me change this view.

Mrs Grace Hickling: It hasn't affected my opinion of the necessity for control measures at all. The one weak link in the chain of public information is the fisheries' argument. It's virtually impossible to say how much a seal eats. They've given us a figure of 15 lb. and it may be five more or five less, but I think that is the weak point. And I do think the

1. The images of a million beloved pets are embodied in one
   new born seal face.

2. Some grey seal mothers are aggressive in the protection of their pups.

3. A grey seal cow suckles her pup.

4. Pups lie about like maggots on a stony beach.

5. A visitor to a breeding colony is scrutinized by anxious faces from the sea.

6. The professional culling of pups is as humane as a slaughterhouse.

8. A crowded grey seal breeding beach.

7. Moulter carcases being removed to the ship for skinning.

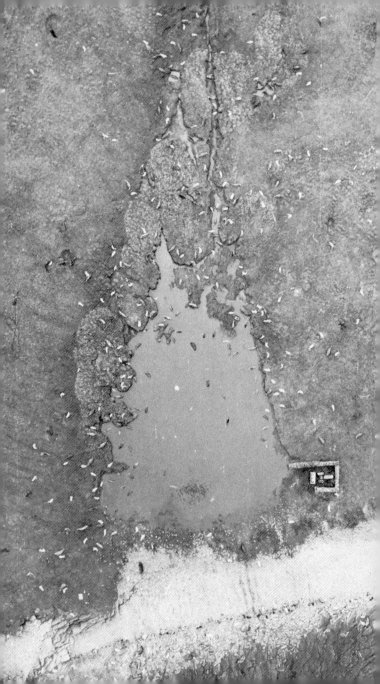

10. The *Kvitungen*, the Norwegian sealing vessel awaiting the start of the cull.

11. Grey seal carcases lie about after a cull of adults and associated pups.

9. Aerial view of an Orkney seal colony.

12. Symbolic of the whole conservation conflict, a man looms large over the helpless pup.

government has to do publicity. We [on the Farne Islands] have agreed to try to produce a brief leaflet so that people can know what's happened. This is just one little example of a public relations exercise, and obviously the government should do a similar thing.

Mr Alan Thornton: The publicity hasn't affected my opinion of the control measures. I have always been against them because there is no justification for them.

Mr Basil B. Parrish: Well, it certainly hasn't changed my view of the justification for the management plan that was drawn up. I personally am very sorry that the publicity has been of the kind that it has and I am afraid it indicates to me that much of the publicity is based on a poor understanding of the actual content of the management plan and its basis.

The Earl of Cranbrook: Considering I was one of those who recommended it, I went up to the Orkney meeting where I heard a great deal said, but I heard no evidence that led me to think that the recommendations made by the Advisory Committee were wrong. I was very surprised by the adverse level of publicity. I mean, these control measures have been going on in Orkney since 1963 – for fifteen years. The licences are given under conditions which ensure humane weapons are used. I've heard no grumbles during the years I've been on the Advisory Committee. I was very surprised that, because we were going to kill some adults and more pups as well, and humanely, that there should be any objection to it.

Question 4. *What effect do you think this cull would have had on our fish stocks?*

Sir Frank Fraser Darling: We don't know, but my guess is that they would have very little. The reason being – and this is where I am appalled at the attitudes of the Scottish fishing laboratory at Torry – they have extrapolated from what they imagine is truth, that the seal eats 15 lb. of fish a day, and that therefore all that fish could be consumed by the human being and that it obviously must be better for it to be used as fish and chips than to be consumed by a seal. My attitude is that that 15 lb. of fish is made up of all manner. I have watched these seals fishing and you see a big bull seal with a six-foot conger eel in his mouth and he is nipping it and the thing doesn't die very quickly. It can lurch itself around and really put up a fight. Is that eel valuable for preserving edible fish? I don't think so!

Sir Peter Scott: If we are talking now about the control measures which were proposed and not carried out, I personally think that they would have had a minimal effect on fishing stocks. I certainly doubt if it would be measurable by comparison with the effect on fish stocks of massive overfishing by man.

Mr W. Nigel Bonner: I'm a seal biologist and not a fisheries biologist, so I can't really give an expert opinion. Grey seals do eat great quantities of fish. I think a reasonable estimate for British grey seals would be a bit over 100,000 tons a year. But no one has ever suggested killing all the seals, so the effect of a cull would account for only a fraction of that figure. On the other hand we must recognize that the fisheries are already hard pressed and can't easily absorb extra pressure from an increasing seal population.

Mrs Grace Hickling: I think maybe only a small amount, but I also think that there are too many seals.

Mr Alan Thornton: I don't think it would have had any measurable effect on our fish stocks whatsoever.

Mr Basil B. Parrish: If by this you mean the particular cull in the Orkneys and North Rona this year, its actual effect on the fish stocks would not have been very large; but it was, of course, only one element of a total management plan spanning a number of years. The effect of the whole plan on the fish stocks would be quite significant, by reducing the amount of exploitable fish consumed by seals and hence providing a larger annual fishery yield, and also – this is most important – it is vitally important to remember that with no management programme the grey seal population in Scottish waters will almost certainly continue to increase, with an inevitable further increase in their consumption of fish, and hence further loss of potential fishery yield.

The Earl of Cranbrook: The only reason we recommended them [the measures] was because we thought they would help to prevent deterioration of our inshore fish stocks.

Question 5. *Do you think the media handled the public interest well?*

Sir Frank Fraser Darling: I don't know. They made enough fuss about it but I don't think they left the inquiring intelligent person with any clarification of the problem.

Sir Peter Scott: Not having been here at the time that it was happening, I'm not really in a position to say. But yes, I think the media probably played a big part in the immediate outcome which I believe *was* in the public interest.

Mr W. Nigel Bonner: No. Of course, the media are for the most part after a good story. Words like massacre are bandied around. We don't talk about a rat-catcher massacring rats. And the fisheries case was hardly stated at all.

Mrs Grace Hickling: Absolutely shocking. I think we would have had the operation carried out efficiently, particularly if the 'Nationwide' people hadn't come into it, and it's just been simply blown up to make a public holiday, so to speak. They proposed this cull last year, nobody said anything about it; they did it on the Monach Isles and there was no fuss at all. Now because it's a nice emotive subject and the media think the public will lap it up, this has happened, and I think it's completely the media that are at fault.

Mr Alan Thornton: I think the media handled the public interest very well.

Mr Basil B. Parrish: It is a very difficult question for me to answer. As one of the scientists involved in the preparation of the management plan I feel bound to say that I feel the media's handling was rather biased towards the anti-culling lobby.

The Earl of Cranbrook: Well, I take *The Times* and the *East Anglian* and neither of them has ever said anything that I didn't think was reasonable. I accept that there were objections, but I didn't hear enough about what they [the media] did to be able to comment about it reasonably or sensibly.

Question 6. *Do you consider seals to be a valuable link in the ocean's ecology?*

Sir Frank Fraser Darling: I am not sure about the ocean's ecology. If you take the immense wastes of ocean, I don't know. But the inshore ecology, yes they are. I imagine that again one's experience is limited. I mean you have got to have fifty years or a hundred years of experience of that situation. So I really don't know, but my guess is that they do have a considerable effect through time.

Sir Peter Scott: Yes. A very important element. Even at the very low number of grey seals that there are; but seals all told – if you include the more numerous species in the north and the south and all around – are, of course, a very significant and important element of the ocean's ecosystems.

Mr W. Nigel Bonner: Seals are predators at the top of the food pyramid and while all parts of an ecosystem are important, one might argue that the value of a species at the top is probably less than those which make up the base. The seal's role as a fish predator has been largely assumed by man and there is no evidence to suggest that when there were far fewer seals, earlier this century, the ecosystem suffered in any way.

Mrs Grace Hickling: Oh, yes. They take the squid and other predatory fish like this and they obviously are a necessary part. And I think you must have a reasonable number.

Mr Alan Thornton: Yes. I think they are, especially because they are at the top of the food chain.

Mr Basil B. Parrish: Because they are part of the total ecosystem and they are preying at a fairly high level in the total food chain they certainly are an important element in the ecosystem.

The Earl of Cranbrook: Oh yes, I think it's absolutely essential to keep our seal population at the maximum level we can without doing damage to our fish stocks.

Question 7. *To what extent do you think the current seal population is responsible for our diminishing fish stocks?*

Sir Frank Fraser Darling: I should say it was rather a ridiculous question. What are *we* doing? The Russians are actually sucking up the fish through pipes into their factory ships, aren't they?

Sir Peter Scott: I answered minimally before and that's what I mean. I don't believe they do have a significant effect.

Mr W. Nigel Bonner: Hardly at all, I would think. The main pressure on fish is by humans and we have to do all we can to control this. There is no reason at all why a reasonable stock of seals should not co-exist with a rational fishing policy.

Mrs Grace Hickling: It is difficult to say, and this seems to be the one point about which people know very little. I should say the problem is largely over fishing, not the seals – the seals do take so much but I don't think it's as much as is made out. No, I don't think the effect is as much as people make out.

Mr Alan Thornton: Seals are not responsible at all.

Mr Basil B. Parrish: Certainly the declines in the main fish stocks exploited around the British Isles cannot be attributed principally to the increase in the seal population. It is well known that during the post-war period the growth of fishing intensity on all of the major stocks has been the principal cause of the fish stock decline. But the predatory effect of seals on the fish resources in the areas around the Scottish coasts is in no sense insignificant.

The Earl of Cranbrook: Grey seals are not deep-sea animals. The depleted stocks about which we are arguing with the Common Market are those taken well off shore by methods of fishing, fish which are only affected by seals if and when they come inshore in Scottish waters. Seals do, though, seriously affect the fish stocks which form the livelihood of inshore fishermen.

Question 8.   *Do you think the fishermen are being fairly represented by those in authority?*

Sir Frank Fraser Darling: No.

Sir Peter Scott: I really don't know enough to know whether they are, but, yes, I think those in authority probably do represent, perhaps over-represent, the views of fishermen who don't really know much of the scientific facts.

Mr W. Nigel Bonner: No I don't. Fisheries have a case which deserves to be put before the public with just as much vigour as the conservation case. This has not been done.

Mrs Grace Hickling: A difficult question – the salmon fishermen are always screaming about the seals. I mean we suffer a great deal here from the local fishing authorities under the water board who want to keep seal numbers down. Yes, I think they get good representation.

Mr Alan Thornton: I think the fishermen are being overrepresented if the proposed management scheme is a measure of their opinion. It is certainly not representative of the feelings of the public at large – but then the fishing industry is not well known for restraint.

Mr Basil B. Parrish: Yes. The government departments which have responsibility for developing and implementing resource management activities very definitely have the interests of the fishing industry in mind.

The Earl of Cranbrook. I hope so. That's all I can say because I really don't know.

Question 9.   *Do you think seals are being made a scapegoat to off-set criticism of overfishing in British waters?*

Sir Frank Fraser Darling: Yes.

Sir Peter Scott: Yes, just that.

Mr W. Nigel Bonner: No.

Mrs Grace Hickling: No. No, I don't think so, necessarily, because there are too many seals and they need controlling for their own good.

Mr Alan Thornton: Yes. I do believe that attention is being shifted away from overfishing and onto seal damage. Damage to fish stocks is caused by humans, not seals. An examination of catch records indicates that all European countries combined catch over 3 million tons of fish annually. The blame for decline rests solely on those who are overfishing. Only strong conservation measures can slow this decline.

Mr Basil B. Parrish: Emphatically, no.

The Earl of Cranbrook: No.

Question 10.   *What effect will this level of emotive publicity have on government control policy?*

Sir Frank Fraser Darling: It is better to think that any politically made decision will always take the easy way. If they feel that the masses are having to pay through the nose for their fish and chips, and they think of some way of getting it at a lower price, they will follow it.

Sir Peter Scott: Well, it has had an effect, of course, already, in bringing about a stay of execution. I think it will make people look much more carefully at the data base, the solid scientific basis for the wild – I call it a wild – figure of the proposed reduction of 50 per cent, which seemed to me not to be based on any tenable scientific data.

Mr W. Nigel Bonner: I hope the government will show confidence in their expert advisers rather than responding at the last moment to uninformed pressure.

Mrs Grace Hickling: Again, this is for the government to say, but I think it will be extremely difficult for them to carry out the culling. I know that from my own experience. I'm certain it has a very bad effect on any measures to control them. They [the government] didn't explain that of course enormous numbers of these young would die anyway, and that they're not taking half the colony, they're merely reducing. I mean they hope to reduce it by a lot, but initially they're not taking all these vast numbers that they talk about, and they've plenty of time to alter their quotas if need be.

Mr Alan Thornton: Now that the government has been forced to accept a new position on grey seals, the united coalition of conservation bodies will require a continuous reassessment of the management policy. I certainly don't think they will try to rush through such a drastic policy again.

Mr Basil B. Parrish: I am afraid I cannot make any useful comment on the question. It is a matter for the government.

The Earl of Cranbrook: It won't prevent me, if I continue to be a member of the Seals Advisory Committee, giving advice which I think is sensible, based on the scientific evidence which was put before it. Now what the government does with that advice is for the government to decide, not me. I think they [the Scottish Office] were in an impossible position; don't forget the Norwegian sealers were going to

use high-velocity rifles on rocky islands, and if
people were going to deliberately place themselves
in the line of fire, or sufficiently close to the line of
fire to be injured by ricochets, I don't see that the
Ministry could have possibly allowed it to go on. I
think the problem here is that the general public
hasn't really realized the background which led the
Minister to make his decision about whether there
would be a cull, and I think somehow it has got to
be got across to the general public.

*Question 11. How do you think the control of seals should be
implemented?*

Sir Frank Fraser Darling: Well, forty years ago I
suggested, in a rather loose way I think – it wasn't
very well thought out – that there should be a small
ship that was a sealing ship, and it should take a toll
of grey seals just before the breeding season. It's
adult seals that we should really want to control,
and, also thinking in terms of conservation of
natural resources, it's these fat oily seals before the
breeding season that are really the most practicable
prey, and this is when the stock of grey seals could
easiest stand the toll being taken. It all sounds
horrible and very opposite to what I am usually
considered to be thinking, but even the calf seals
which you would kill at that time, their white-
coated pup which would have to be removed from
the dead seal at that time is more valuable, if it's a
white coat you want, than would be a seal pup a
week or two weeks or even three weeks old. In fact
it's an absolute waste to kill seals at a week or two
old – they will have already started to shed their
white coat. The grey seal has unfortunately bio-
logically failed to shed its white coat in the uterus
which the common seal does. It sounds extraordi-
nary that this should be the criterion, but I never-

theless feel that the grey seal has not the training and education that the common seal has. In fact I would say that the common seal has more intelligence than the grey seal.

Sir Peter Scott: Well I'm not sufficiently expert to know what is the best way of reducing grey seals. It's not my subject so I don't really know, I'm afraid, when you should kill what or what is the best way to do it. I do accept that there may be occasions when there are conflicts of interest in conservation itself, like the Farne Islands, where a kill of some sort may be necessary. Where if you're to retain what is regarded as a diverse ecosystem, you may have to undertake a culling programme, which reduces the numbers of any one species that may be destroying the habitat of some other species. For example, the increase of breeding grey seals may limit the available breeding space for eider ducks or terns. But exactly how you limit the seals' population increase is not my expertise.

Mr W. Nigel Bonner: I think that the proposals put forward were the best available under the circumstances. They would have been better if they had been put into force earlier, before it became necessary to reduce the seals by such a dramatic number. I also think that the proposals fall into line with good conservational practice.

Mrs Grace Hickling: I think the way it was going to be done in Orkney. So far as Orkney's concerned you must kill adults, there's no doubt about that, and the Norwegians are efficient if they have proper backing-up. They'll do it very well. The business of taking youngsters is far too slow, it has very, very little effect. I think they've been taking 750 pups in Orkney annually since the early 1960s and the population has increased, as you know, instead of going down. So although you can take very large numbers of youngsters, and you may do some controlling, you have a much worse chance of seeing the effects on the population as a whole, whereas if you take adults you can get numbers down more quickly.

Mr Alan Thornton: I don't know. It's up to the biologists to perfect the implementation of management – if it's proved to be necessary.

Mr Basil B. Parrish: I see no real alternative to culling as the means of controlling seal numbers at a level below their maximum, natural population size. This can be approached either by the culling of pups or of adults or, as in the present management plan, a combination of the two. Our experience in the past has shown that pup culling alone failed to achieve the desired results and it is most unlikely that the objectives of the present management plan could be achieved by it. I therefore consider that a combination of adult and pup culling is the most appropriate management control measure. In order to maximize the scientific information which is obtained in the course of such a cull, which is an important objective of the present plan, I think that a combination of pup culling and adult culling in which the latter is divided between breeding colony and elsewhere outside the breeding season would, if practicable, probably be the most appropriate approach.

The Earl of Cranbrook: I think that probably the combination of adult with pup cull is a good way of doing it because you're having your cake and eating it. You're looking a little bit ahead with the pup cull, you're looking at the present with the adult cull, both of which you could stop or modify at any time. But I think just as with every other animal that can increase in numbers to such an extent that it does damage to one or other of man's activities, it may well be that we've got to fix the level at which we think the seals ought to be kept, and keep them at that level.

Question 12. Do you think this control programme is derived solely from objective scientific recommendation or are power politics also involved?

Sir Frank Fraser Darling: I certainly don't think that it's from objective scientific observation. It's not, it's as plain as that, if you are tackling a practical problem, and not producing objective scientific observation.

Sir Peter Scott: I don't think it's derived solely from objective scientific recommendation, because I don't think the scientific data are there for an objective recommendation to exist; and secondly I wouldn't be at all surprised, although I have no evidence to say that I know this, if power politics were not involved.

Mr W. Nigel Bonner: Control of grey seals in Britain was first recommended by the Consultative Committee on Grey Seals and Fisheries in 1963. This was based on the scientific evidence available at the time. Since then, instead of stabilizing the population, it has increased, as has the scientific evidence. So this cull isn't a new idea, it's just an endorsement of earlier policies and an earlier interpretation of the scientific evidence.

Mrs Grace Hickling: No, quite definitely not. Anyone who reads the papers, especially the current papers in the *Journal of Applied Ecology*, will know it's based entirely on scientific evidence.

Mr Alan Thornton: I don't think there was anything objective about the recommendation. I don't know enough about the English political system to say whether there are power politics involved, although it certainly has been suggested to me.

Mr Basil B. Parrish: Certainly the former. The present culling programme was drawn up on the basis of scientific information on the growth of the seal population and their predatory effects on exploited fishery resources. This information was considered in depth by the Seals Advisory Committee, and subsequently by NERC, which advised the Secretary of State that a management plan, aimed at reducing the grey seal population in Scottish waters to its mid-sixties' level, involving the culling of adult seals in the breeding season together with pups, would be an appropriate management measure to adopt.

The Earl of Cranbrook: This really is suggesting that the advice which the Seals Advisory Committee gave was to placate the government, and that's nonsense. The 1959 Committee reported that the crunch had come [with the seal population] before there was any possibility or any suggestion that there was any ulterior motive behind it. The present Committee has waited for more evidence and did not take any precipitate action in spite of evidence about cod-worm, pressure on fisheries and the like. From 1970 to 1977 we have seen the population of grey seals in Scottish waters double to twice what it was when our predecessors said that it was already too large. We then decide that we ought to advise a cull in such a way that if we find it's not necessary, if the premises on which we base our cull are wrong, we could stop at any moment. Now I think that is the right way of looking at it, and I don't think any outside pressure would have swayed the Committee's interpretation of the evidence.

CHAPTER 7

A Personal View

There seems small doubt that the seal-struck British
public would be happier if they (Greenpeace) succeeded
– even at the cost of a pricier fish-finger.

Sunday Telegraph editorial
15 October 1978

So we come back to the basic public reaction of disapproval, a
reaction which was there before either Greenpeace or any of the
other objectors began their propaganda campaigns. There is probably truth in the suggestion that they are themselves an extension
of that reaction, albeit a logical and carefully thought-out one.
Even after the controversy had run its course in the Orkneys and
the press coverage had been so widespread and comprehensive,
samples of public opinion showed no real absorption of the facts or
the justifications for either course of action. Instead they endorsed
the instinctive revulsion felt so strongly by so many to killing seals.

It seems to me that the real heat of opposition comes from those
people who have identified with seals either through personal contact with the animals or through television or photographs in
books and magazines. No one will dispute the power of the illus-
tration in journalism. The next level of opposition comes from
those who may never have seen a seal or a film of one, and who
may not necessarily know anything about them, but whose own
existence is so remote from pest control, or the killing of animals
of any sort, that all destruction of life is looked upon to be un-
savoury. But it is the third category of opposition which is the
most interesting. An opinion poll taken in an agricultural community where animal control in one form or another is a daily affair
revealed curiously powerful opposition to killing seals. When
pressed to explain their own reactions, none of the people I spoke

to, farmers, farm workers, foresters and villagers in several small communities, were able to give any better a justification for their feelings than anyone else. And yet, in several instances, they had united and eagerly signed petitions to send to the Scottish Office.

Man's attitude towards the seal is, in fact, remarkably similar to his attitude towards the dog, and there are interesting connections between the two animals.

Man emerged, we now think, as the primitive man we called *Homo erectus*, some 400,000 years ago. The classical find of *Homo erectus* was made in China. He is Peking man and we know for certain that he was a man and he used fire. From the same period we have the remarkable Laszlo Vertes find at Vertesszöllös in western Hungary in 1965. Amongst the bones of sabre-toothed tigers, woolly rhinoceroses and beavers, Vertes found the traces of fire and indications of regular hearths in the same deposit. Man the hunter, complete with stone implements and a settled community, had mastered fire and sat picking the bones of his prey around these early ancestral forest clearings. What we also know from later stone-age finds is that some of those discarded bones were cracked by the canine jaw. Wild dogs have been camp followers ever since the first hungry hound discovered how to survive by daring to slink in towards the dying hearth and snatch up a discarded bone. It was a short step to domestication; although whether man realized the advantage in having dogs about his camp before he found an orphaned cub and reared it instead of killing and eating it, we can only guess. All we do know is that long before he domesticated any grazing beast he had a dog at his side. The dog has been there ever since. So man and dog have been together, in true symbiosis, longer than any other human animal combination, and the advantages for both species have only served to cement their relationship more and more strongly.

Now, with the help of skilled museum scientists and taxonomists, we discover that the seals we see around our shores in Britain are direct ancesters of the same dog-like mammal which evolved to be our own camp follower. Certainly the time gap is enormous. The dog-seals returned to the sea (animal life is thought to have come from it in the first place) some tens of millions of years ago, whereas man and dog went into partnership less than half a million years ago. But nevertheless those endearing features we admire in our own dogs are pressingly evident in seals: the wet nose and the wide liquid eyes; the dog muzzle and head; the inquisitive nature, and, more specifically, dentitional, anatomical and sociological similarities with dog types of land mammal, all of which contribute evidence to this ancestral association.

It may be that these physical resemblances are responsible for man's affection for the seal. Is it also possible that somewhere in the collective unconscious of each of us lies a profound emotional link with the dog, based, not like our present relationship on convenience and whim, but on the hard reality of survival at a time when man was by no means lord of all he surveyed, and that this relationship has been transferred to the seal because of the common ancestry of the two animals? We cannot tell, but it would account for the strong ties with man manifested in legends concerning the seal.

In his remarkable book *The People of the Sea* David Thomson searches for the truth behind the seal legend. His journey through Ireland and the Western Isles takes him to the heart of those communities which have persecuted seals for centuries to facilitate their own survival. What is revealing in this travelogue is that amongst these remote Gaelic communities there exists a deep-founded mythology about the seals.

> 'I am a man upon the land,
> I am a selchie on the sea . . .'

These lines from an ancient folk song provide the essence of the myth: that seal and man are in some way spiritually interchangeable, a clear indication that a strong subconscious link, consciously unexplainable, may exist between seal and man.

Even in the recent dispute in the Orkneys, islesmen from Orkney, Shetland and the Western Isles who owe their entire livelihood to fishing and who might understandably have found in favour of some measure of control of seals declined to give the cull their support. One Shetland fisherman speaking in an interview on Radio Highland in October said: 'Folklore in Shetland says that old fishermen come back as seals and there would be a

grave danger that if I were shooting seals that I might be shooting
my grandfather!'

But the existence of this instinct throws only a glimmer of light
on the conservationist opposition, which is formidable. Whatever
the particular *raison d'être* of the organizations involved, there is
a powerful body of scientific expertise in their ranks. Greenpeace,
the World Wildlife Fund, the Fauna Preservation Society, the
Scottish Wildlife Trust, the Society for the Promotion of Nature
Conservation, the Council for Nature, and the International Union
for the Conservation of Nature all possess the nowadays essential
core of scientific staff, from straightforward biologists and zoologists through to recognized academic authorities of international
standing, and the modern style of demographer naturalists who
translate field work into statistics. Their combined experience and
ability is far greater than that of any government department or
research team, although their expertise may not be as specific. A
further important point is that several of the specialist seal scientists whose work has contributed evidence used by the proposers
of the culling programmes are also council members or advisers to
the independent conservation bodies opposing it. Clearly the wool
is not going to be pulled over many eyes in this camp. How, then,
have they arrived at a different interpretation of the evidence from
the Natural Environment Research Council and the Department
of Agriculture and Fisheries' scientists?

To a certain extent it can be said that some of these independent conservation bodies must, for their own existence, adopt the
view of the majority of their membership, just as a government
must represent its electorate. Even from my own researches since
the Orkney row in October 1978 I have found these survival tactics in use in defiance of a rational scientific assessment. But even
though this is the case in some instances, it is not an important
factor. It merely endorses what we already know – that the public
are reacting instinctively. And it is made even more insignificant
by the plain fact that notably Greenpeace and the IUCN are not
membership organizations. In a current circular Greenpeace Ltd in
London openly rebut the concept of public membership in a for-
mal style. 'We do not have any official membership as such as we
feel Greenpeace to be more of a movement than an official body

with members, etc. The amount of time and energy involved in assembling and maintaining membership files we feel would be better spent in organizing campaigns. Just by supporting our work you automatically become part of this worldwide movement, toward greater environmental preservation.'

The new style of all-comers-welcome action-group is completely immune to criticisms of member influence or member catching, and it is a good thing that, in this instance, Greenpeace took the leading role in the public eye.

So this difference of opinion would appear not to be the reaction of the instinctively concerned public. 'We question the scientific justification for this level of cull,' cry the independent bodies in unison, and 'I am satisfied on the evidence that action is necessary,' comes echoing back from Mr Bruce Millan.

To assess the evidence is, as I have already explained, a long and laborious task and it is certain that the man in the street will never undertake it. At the time of writing it is being done by two scientists appointed by the Council for Nature and by several other researchers working for independent groups. It will be interesting to compare their findings when they are eventually published.

To present my own view I shall borrow the headings used by Dr E. Barton Worthington's Consultative Committee Report published by the Nature Conservancy in 1963 (reproduced in full in Appendix 3). This document stands at the threshold of seal controversy in Britain, and, although it is fifteen years old, it is still extremely relevant to the whole issue. It is also an excellent measure of how slowly, even in our dizzy era of computers and technology, the accumulation of seal biological data has been. The fifteen years have given us improved population calculation methods, broader life tables, increases in tagging returns and some new computations of fisheries damage. No great revelations have emerged, despite redoubled efforts and expenditure, in the investigation of our largest mammal. To measure this against the progress made in other mammal studies reveals a horrifying discrepancy which would seem to point to the inadequacy of seal biologists.

It just so happens that the Mammal Society of the British Isles published its first handbook of British Mammals in 1964, less than a year after the Consultative Committee report. This year, in 1978, the Mammal Society published a second edition with a foreword by H. N. Southern and I. J. Linn, both academics who have laid the foundations of mammal study in Britain. In a twenty-page introduction to the new edition entitled 'The Study of British Mammals 1964–1976' these two authors proclaim the remarkable advances in this field of zoology. In this article seals are mentioned twice, firstly with reference to Professor Hewer's work in achieving a life table by examining large samples of teeth from seal carcases, but acknowledging that the result is not accurate, and secondly, applauding the work of the Seals Research Division of the NERC, for producing more accurate population estimates of grey seals. Beside the numerous other references to work on terrestrial mammals the seal researchers seem to have done little. Foxes, bats, mice and voles, squirrels, mink, otters and even the diminutive pygmy shrew have been plotted, graphed, tabulated, caught, measured, followed and counted, all to the great advantage of science, but the poor old seals have benefited from few of these molestations. The reasons are nothing whatever to do with any inadequacy on the part of the dedicated researchers. They are because seals are elusive, unfollowable, huge, unpredictable, and mysterious and live in another medium among the most inclement, rockiest and far flung extremities of our islands. The fox and the shrew biologist has an easy job in comparison, and because of this the carefully researched logic of the Consultative Committee on Grey Seals and Fisheries holds good fifteen years later.

1. POPULATION OF GREY SEALS The 1963 Report finds that grey seals are locally abundant around British shores and that numbers have increased substantially since the Protection Acts of 1914 and 1932. In relation to the other thirty-two species of pinnipedia in the world the grey seal is seen to be one of the less numerous.

In 1978 this is still true, but we now have a very good idea how many seals there are and how fast they are increasing.

2. THE RANGE OF MOVEMENTS The 1963 Report states that the tagging programme has provided a picture of dis-

persal of first-year animals from breeding grounds and very little interchange between Farnes and northern Scottish populations.

In 1978, no change, but more information is available to endorse this and give some insight into the age structure of populations.

3. BREEDING BIOLOGY The 1963 Report says that information is not available for constructing accurate life tables for each sex. Certain assumptions were made that grey seals correspond to Pribilof fur seals which have been intensively studied. The fact is reported that the mean annual numbers of seals in a colony can be determined by multiplying the number of pups born by 3.5.

In 1978 we have achieved considerable advances in this field because it is the one time of year when the seal can be scrutinized. But nothing has radically altered except that we now have accurate life tables as well as a far greater weight of research to substantiate breeding facts. We can now accurately predict short-term population increases for some colonies.

4. THE FOOD OF GREY SEALS The 1963 Report states that seals feed upon whatever is most readily available and it is probable that this will be predominantly fish. It concludes that even though feeding activity is suspended or reduced during the breeding season and moult, intensive and dispersed feeding takes place throughout the spring and summer, most of which is likely to be of potential commercial value. It also contains the caution that 'the lack of direct evidence precludes a direct assessment of the effect of seals on fish stocks' . . . and 'a determination of the proportion of fish eaten by seals which would otherwise be available to, or taken by, man'.

In 1978, no change. While we do know more about the seal diet, such assessments which have been made of the effect of seals on fish stocks and how much of that fish would be available to man are far from conclusive.

5. THE EFFECT OF SEALS ON FISHING GEAR AND FISH CATCH The 1963 Report lists 6–20 per cent

damaged fish from fixed-net salmon fisheries and substantial
complaints from drift-net ones, with special reference to fish dis-
figuration. It cites measures to reduce direct damage by institut-
ing synthetic fibre nets and seal scaring by rifle fire and under-
water explosions. In the case of the white fish industry it states
that no numerical measure of damage can be given, but suggests
that it may be appreciable.

In 1978 the scene has changed. Synthetic fibres have greatly re-
duced net damage to salmon fisheries, and recent increases in
catch have made the existing level of seal damage to fish a sup-
portable natural hazard. But the white fish industry has taken over
the main cause for complaint, although evidence is scarce and as-
sessments of damage are still very speculative.

6. THE TRANSMISSION OF COD-WORM The 1963
Report links the grey seal firmly with the infestation of cod by this
undesirable worm. It states that although only a small proportion
of cod landed in Britain is infested it is nevertheless clear that the
parasites could affect the marketability of fish.

In 1978 we know that despite the dramatic rise in seal numbers in
British waters the incidence of cod-worm infestation has not in-
creased proportionately. It is now considered to be a further natu-
ral hazard which is perhaps supportable by the fishing industry.

7. THE SELECTION OF METHODS OF CON-
TROL The 1963 Report weighs up the advantages between killing cows on the breeding haul-outs and killing pups.

In 1978 there is no third method available.

8. THE PRACTICE OF SEAL CULLING The 1963
Report dismisses the use of captive-bolt pistols, clubs, narcotic
darts and various rifles and pistols. It comes down in favour of a
Webley Scott pistol as used by veterinary surgeons or a .22 rifle
at point-blank range for shooting pups in the back of the head,
and only a high-velocity rifle as used for red deer for killing
adults, which should not be shot in the heart.

In 1978, no change.

9. THE UTILIZATION OF PRODUCTS OF SEAL CONTROL The 1963 Report values the first white coat of the pup at about £1–£2.50 and the silver grey pelt of a moulter at £3. The other products of value are refined blubber oil for the food and soap industries and livers and meat and bone meal for the mammal foodstuffs industry.

In 1978 the values have risen to about £10 for both skins. Blubber oil is still marketable.

10. RECOMMENDATIONS FOR MANAGEMENT AND CONTROL OF GREY SEALS IN GREAT BRITAIN AND FOR REDUCING THE DAMAGE WHICH THEY CAUSE TO FISHERIES The 1963 Report says cull now, selectively and carefully on the Orkneys and Farnes in the breeding season. 'In making this recommendation the Committee recognizes that the operations must be experimental in the sense that the effect on fisheries of these measures cannot be predicted with any precision.' 'The policy of controlling numbers of seals should be subject to revision at any time if information shows this to be desirable.'

In 1978 precisely the same recommendations were put forward by the Seals Advisory Committee with the exception that the Farne Islands are being managed separately by the National Trust, and some of the Hebridean colonies have been included with Orkney. The difference lies in the number of seals: a British total of some 36,000 then and 70,000 now.

The small print of the 1963 Report shows that the recommendations would effect a reduction of the total breeding population of British grey seals by one-quarter (i.e. to 75 per cent of their 1963 status) over five years. Given that there were approximately 36,000 grey seals in British waters at that time, the five-year reduction would reduce this to approximately 27,000. In 1977/8, the total number of seals in Britain is approximately 70,000, and the plan to halve this over six years brings us, in round figures, to 35,000 – which is, to all intents and purposes, the same figure as the 1963 Report found to be too many, and is 8,000 seals more than they had hoped to have by 1968.

There is no doubt that the lobby in 1963 to control seals was from the salmon fisheries. Now, it will be argued, the salmon industry has largely solved its seal problem. This is true, although salmon are still being damaged both in and out of the nets by marauding seals. It is the white fish industry which has taken the lobby over, and, as the Fishermen's Federations will gladly admit, their concern has grown with the increasing population of seals, but the proof needed to substantiate commercial losses is very much harder to come by than in the salmon industry.

One question remains unanswered. Why have the independent conservation bodies raised no objection to seal control before? Why not in 1977, when the same Norwegian firm, G. C. Rieber, came to the Hebrides to do a similar cull on the main breeding colonies there? Why not back in 1963, when there were far fewer seals and when the 25 per cent reduction was just as drastic to the total seal population as the present measures? And why not at any time in between when on several occasions seal control has been suggested and debated?

It is true that a number of the bodies concerned in the current controversy were not in existence in 1963. The Scottish Wildlife Trust and Greenpeace are two recently established movements which were not around to make an active stand at that time. But others were, and it is perhaps a fair criticism to suggest that they should have been watching the seal control lobby rise and keeping abreast of the research programme for many years. It is clear from looking down the published aims and objectives of several of these organizations that basic watchdog work is an important function and in some instances it has been badly neglected.

But the real reason for the sudden reaction in 1978 is, I suspect, nothing to do with British seals nor British conservation movements. It is because of the harp seal row in Canada.

Unlike the grey seal, the harp seal (*Phoca groenlandica*) is one of the world's most numerous seals. There are thought to be over five million in existence, although just how many remains the centrepoint of its own very fraught controversy. The harp seal has no real home. It ranges up and down the ice edge of the Arctic throughout the year. To breed, it hauls out onto the ice in the spring at three main stations: the north-east coast of Newfoundland and in the Gulf of St Lawrence; in the Greenland sea around Jan Mayen; and in the White Sea. It is persecuted by man throughout its range, but it is the Newfoundland and Gulf of St Lawrence populations which are the largest and the most questioned. Here, each spring for centuries, the Newfoundlanders have harvested the white-coated ice-bound pups for skins. In recent years this annual slaughter, which has become the greatest kill of concentrated wild mammals in the world, has attracted international attention.

As the kill quotas have slowly risen, so has the anti-kill indignation of the Canadian public. By 1975 the sealers were the most unpopular section of any community in the country and the press gave constant support to the case for stopping the hunt. In the last two years, however, the position has considerably altered. In 1977 it was reported in the Canadian press that an international movement to stop the harp seal cull had made enormous profits from its campaigns, to the tune of almost half a million dollars surplus at the end of 1975. Quite suddenly things turned against the preservationists. The Canadian government endorsed a resolution supporting the seal hunt and much support which was previously given to the anti-kill league was withdrawn.

Apart from the moral issue about whether seal pups should be killed at all, the main axis of controversy is whether or not the harp seal is in danger. The kill quotas fixed by the Canadian government are large: 160,000 in 1977 and 180,000 in 1978. One body of scientists say the population can support this and still increase, and another says it can't. The problem is counting. The areas in question are hostile in the early spring – bitterly cold and often fog-bound. Counting pups and adults is a very difficult job, and is complicated by the harp seal being spread over vast areas of ice. No one really knows the accurate pup-production figures and it looks as though scientists are likely to go on arguing about it for a good few years yet.

The latest development in the harp seal row is the most worrying one. Just before the 1977 hunt began the Seal Protection Act was rushed through the Canadian Parliament. It is a curious title for a curious piece of legislation. It is not clear how the seals are going to be protected by it. It makes illegal the landing of any air-

craft or helicopter within half a mile from any seal on the ice.
Half a mile is a long way on pack-ice and this effectively prevents
the anti-hunt lobby, like Greenpeace, who have actively demonstrated on the ice to stop the hunt, from getting there in time to
stop the killing. The Act further prevents any aircraft from flying
at an altitude of less than 2,000 feet over any seal on the ice. This
means that aerial surveys cannot be made and it prevents the press
or the 'antis' from knowing what is going on.

As if this is not enough, it is now proposed to make it illegal for
pressmen to cover the seal hunt in person without the prior permission of the Minister. Along with this goes a massive public
relations campaign in support of the sealing industry. Its justification is the commercial value of the skins and the employment the
sealing provides in a difficult employment area, but already it is
widely rumoured that the campaign is costing more than the loss
of revenue and unemployment payments ever could.

In a recent statement Greenpeace told their own story:

In 1976, Greenpeace members went onto the ice floes in Labrador in
Canada to protect harp seal pups from the clubs of licensed hunters.
They stood between seals and sealers and in front of sealing vessels to
block access to the herds. Their helicopters were seized by fisheries officials. 169,000 seals were killed that year. In 1978, Greenpeace protested
the hunt on two fronts. Members of Greenpeace Vancouver were arrested trying to protect seals with their bodies, thus challenging the
controversial Seal Protection Act (!) which prohibits any interference
with the hunt. They are awaiting trial at present. In Norway, members
of Greenpeace UK, Greenpeace France and Norwegian supporters
chained themselves to sealing vessels preparing to leave for Newfoundland in an attempt to stop their departure. They were blasted with fire
hoses by the crews, had garbage thrown on them and were arrested. The
action brought the hunt issue to the attention of the Norwegian people,
since the story was carried by every major Norwegian newspaper as well
as on television. Members of Greenpeace Toronto took a similar action
by setting out in inflatables to stop sealing ships from entering the harbour at Newfoundland. They were also met with fire hoses and garbage.
The final kill was 90,453 (harp and hood seals as of 10 April 1978) –
many fewer than the quota of 195,000 set for the year. Bad weather and
poor ice conditions prevented the hunters from a larger take.

Because of this harp seal action and their consequent identity with seals Greenpeace were bound to look hard at the British government's plan to cull grey seals in 1978. This they did, and decided that, as in the harp seal issue, the justification was inadequate. Their own statement continues:

In early October the *Rainbow Warrior* went to the Orkney Islands to the north of the Scottish mainland in a successful bid to halt the Department of Agriculture and Fisheries of Scotland Grey Seal Management Plan, until its scientific justification can be properly and publicly discussed. This year's programme would have involved the killing of 900 cows and their associated pups plus 4,000 moulted pups. The ultimate aim of this plan would reduce the world population of grey seals by a third. Conservation and protection of fisheries is the justification given for this drastic proposal. Greenpeace is opposed to the cull and the attempt to shift the blame for declining fish stocks from human overfishing to the seals.

After a week of constant surveillance of the *Kvitungen* (the Norwegian sealing vessel hired to take most of the quota) by the *Rainbow Warrior* and vigils kept on most of the seal rookeries by local people from the group Selkie, the Secretary of State for Scotland withdrew the Norwegian boat. The Western Isles and Orkney quota of 2,000 moulted pups was not withdrawn, but this is a local hunt which has been going on for several years, and is not seen to have the impact on the seal population as would the taking of adults and the larger number of pups. The local quota had previously been incorporated in the six-year plan.

The Orkney campaign result was a major and internationally recognized victory, not just for the seals, but for the many people and organizations who have striven to bring change to such environmentally unsound policies in the past.

Suddenly the British situation was a gaping sore, like the Canadian one – even though they are as far apart in purpose, application and risk as are Labrador and Orkney. We *do* know how many grey seals there are; and we *do* know that the cull quotas would not affect the viability of the breeding units in question. Grey seal colonies have sturdily withstood far greater impact spread over a far longer period than the six-year plan. And we are not commercially exploiting our grey seals for profit, or employment, or anything else. The action is a conservation one: the conservation of fish stocks and of seals – quite the reverse of the harp seal case. And, most important of all, we have no undemocratic legislation preventing objectors from objecting or independent assessors from assessing for themselves. But we do run the risk of forcing the government to take this sort of step if we are not very careful.

It is an old dichotomy. If the issue is finally proved to be right, any action is justified, but if it is later proved to have been entirely misguided, what damage will have been done by that action?

If what happened here in the Orkneys in 1978 is eventually proved to have been correct, then the independent conservationist bodies will have added stature indeed, but if, as I fear, the reverse is true, then many of our national conservation bodies which have previously been held in high esteem will lose face, and the task facing our national conservation agency, the Nature Conservancy Council, and the other government departments concerned will be made far more difficult.

The implication of this would seem to be that Greenpeace and their supporters did not know what they were doing. This is true, although I do not hold them entirely to blame. The error seems to me to lie in the timing. For many years now there has been an unwillingness on the part of those involved in seal research and control to reveal their full hand to the press and the public because, as we have seen, the public have a history of instinctive reaction towards seals which can be damaging and insulting to scientists and workers alike. It has become a standard. Only recently I was told by a seal researcher that on one occasion in Britain in recent years complicated plans had been drawn up to lure public attention away from one particular experimental culling programme. This is understandable in the case of a small experiment, but for a major management exercise it is unforgivable.

The Department of Agriculture and Fisheries have seriously neglected the public relations side of their seal control work ever since it was first proposed. In the 1978 row press notices were woolly and, if not evasive, they were not openly forthcoming. No published document explaining the six-year plan in detail, and giving the supporting evidence, exists at the date of writing. (The author's copy was provided for him by a member of the Seals Advisory Committee.) There is nothing more provocative than high-handedness and reticence. I believe the Scottish Office are guilty of both of these. It is a long time since the 1963 Nature Conservancy Report and, anyway, it is out of print. HMSO was unable to help the author obtain a copy. Museum and library copies might not be readily released. The case for re-printing it in an updated form before the culling programme was even announced seems basic. But this was not done. It is not surprising that Greenpeace and other organizations began to wonder why the evidence was not broadly and collectively published. Nor is it surprising that they should have appealed for a one-year moratorium in which to find it and examine it for themselves. When that was refused they were left with little alternative but to present opposition in line with their beliefs. It was blind of the Scottish Office to imagine for one moment that they would not. Less than a year before, they were defying the Canadian law on the ice and chaining themselves to sealing vessels in Norway. It was also blind of the Scottish Office not to have realized that seal killing of any sort is both fashionable and news at the moment on both sides of the Atlantic. The Canadian row has been actively followed in Europe and Britain and the shops are well stocked with books about it. Brigitte Bardot has seen to that. It was certain that if a confrontation of any sort took place here over any seal it would make headline news, and, just as the government caught the independent conservation bodies with their research trousers down, so did Greenpeace and its allies catch the Scottish Office in the nude over public opinion.

The result was panic. The public panicked, the conservationist lobby panicked, and the press, whose staple diet is panic, loved every minute of it, indulging themselves in the discomfort of the bureaucrats and the glory of the independents.

The only people who did not panic, to their credit, were the scientists of the NERC and the Fishermen's Federations. Both of these groups foresaw the immense damage which could be done by a hot and unnecessary flare-up, and played their parts calmly and in low profile.

The harp seal issue has become an ugly affair of international status. Canada is facing trade sanctions in some countries (such as France) because of it. We do not want that to happen here.

Above all, we should not lose sight of the singular fact that a Commonwealth country, closely associated with the UK, has proposed press censorship to control coverage of a seal hunt. Conservation must not become a political sore. It must work with governments not in open opposition to them if it is to progress as it must. It is a powerful and scientifically based movement which is gathering enormous world-wide momentum and its reputation and its achievements depend upon the skill and rationale of its proponents. A compromise is almost always progress and should be accepted as such. After all, conservation itself is a compromise.

CHAPTER 8

A Summary

The question of all questions for mankind – the
problem which underlies all others and which is more
deeply interesting than any other – is the ascertainment
of the place which man occupies in nature and of relations
to the universe of things.

Thomas Henry Huxley

The need for seal control

There is a growing concern among scientists and fishermen that
the effect of the conservation controls currently being employed
by the fishing industry by catch quotas, mesh regulations and the
herring ban is being seriously undermined by an expanding population of grey seals. The collected international evidence of their
impact on fish stocks cannot be shrugged off. Fraser Darling first
recommended grey seal control in 1935, the Barton Worthington
Consultative Committee again proposed control in 1963 and the
Cranbrook Seals Advisory Committee produced the current recommendations in 1977. An effective measure against the present
increase in Scottish grey seals must now be overdue for basic fish
food resource conservation and for significant political reasons.

The scientific basis

While there are at present (and are bound to be for a good many
years yet) some assumptions allied to the scientific basis which
cannot be readily confirmed or refuted, the broad base of information gathered in complete scientific integrity in Great Britain
and overseas is quite sufficient upon which to found a safe man-

agement control programme. The Bonner and Hickling 1971 Grey
Seal Management Plan has been accepted for several years by the
National Trust for the Farne Islands, and, although it is not a
fishery protection measure, it has established methods and
standards which can safely be applied to any other known colony.

The six-year plan for Orkney and the Hebrides

I believe this plan was produced by scientists for scientific consideration and was correspondingly politically naïve. It is fair and
soundly based for what it sets out to achieve, and has adequate
built-in safety clauses which require the constant monitoring of the
impact it produces. Given the seal colonies in question, their geographical situation and the fishing interests affected by those
colonies, it is expedient and practical. But its serious flaw lies in
its total oblivion to current international feeling about seals and
the political application of the plan.

The application of the plan

In so far as it was the duty of the Department of Agriculture and
Fisheries for Scotland to administer the plan, and the Scottish
Office to authorize it, there were serious errors of judgement. At
the time of writing no document detailing the management plan
has been published or proffered for assessment. It was only to be
expected that independent conservation bodies would require to
examine the proposals and there was no proper facility provided
for this. Much of the ire of the opposition was induced by this
oversight. Again, the international temperature of seal control was
apparently neither gauged nor considered. The volatility of the
British public on matters concerning seals and the present fashion
for direct-action opposition appears to have been completely
overlooked despite a long history of objection within Britain.

The insistence of the Secretary of State for Scotland throughout
the October 1978 conflict that the cull was scientifically well justified may have been correct, but it was of little help to those who
had no opportunity of examining it for themselves. To those shut

out by this high-handedness it must have appeared that there was some political intrigue afoot.

The risks

Given that the recommendations of the Natural Environment Research Council's Sea Mammals Research Unit would have been adhered to throughout the six years of the control plan, the risk of permanently damaging the grey seal's stability in the areas concerned is almost negligible. The only risk admitted is that too heavy an impact on any one of a series of breeding colonies might tend to spread the seal population into further territory currently unoccupied, and possibly to areas where future seal control and population monitoring might be more complex and geographically more difficult than at present.

The much more abstract risk of setting unwieldy precedents for culling any animal which comes into conflict with man's interests, as strongly put forward by many of the environmentalist opposition, implies the broad assumption that those specialist scientists whose jobs and reputations stand by the objectivity and competence of their work are not capable of treating each case with the apparent and singular diligence which has been applied to seal research over the past thirty years. The widely claimed threat to sea-bird colonies if seal culling is permitted completely overlooks the quite separate roles that sea-birds play in their ecosystem and the important difference in trophic level at which they feed. It is almost like saying that deer control in forestry is a serious threat to crossbill populations because they also feed on trees.

The humanitarian concern for the prevention of cruelty

Having spoken to cruelty prevention officers present in seal culls, and in particular during the 1977 Monach Isles cull by G. C. Rieber, and having some first-hand knowledge and experience of ballistics and deer control by comparable means, I am convinced that the Norwegian marksmen, their weapons and their back-up team have become efficient at a culling system which is as humane as it can be. This view is also shared by the Scottish Society for the Prevention of Cruelty to Animals (see Appendix 1, p. 125), who have made themselves active monitors of seal culling in Scotland. The possibility of leaving wounded animals can be discounted and the risk of leaving orphaned pups to starve, while it does exist, is known and guarded against, and anyway is a natural phenomenon in any seal colony. It is fair to say that the conditions for the cull are likely to be less stressful for the seals than those for cattle in a slaughterhouse.

On the other hand there is a record of cruelty among licensed and illegal pup hunters which is undesirable. As long as that method of pup culling is used, there will be some suffering.

The action by animal welfare and environmentalist factions

The action to oppose the cull was brought about by the Orcadian group 'Selkie', who called in Greenpeace. There followed a chain reaction which culminated in blanket opposition from many organizations, very few of which had made any serious attempt to examine the case for or against seal control in Britain. What 'Selkie' really did was to reveal some reputable organizations, straight away to the scientific world, and perhaps later to the world at large, as inadequately prepared (and therefore unqualified to oppose) and precipitate in action. Some people will always consider the effect of this to have been positive, but my own opinion is that organizations which should, by 1978, have been in possession of a considered policy on seal-control measures which have been proposed for fifteen years, based on their own assessment of scientific literature which is constantly available to them, and were found to be totally lacking any policy of their own, have lost face and stature in the eyes of many people, and, if the outcome of the opposition is later seen to be damaging to the conservation movement as a whole, they must be held partly responsible.

Nevertheless it is important that these independent bodies exist and that they should continue to question all conservation issues from their own standpoint. They are an essential watchdog against political, commercial and accidental exploitation of the environment, and, by and large, do a very good job. It is sincerely to be hoped that no damage to them or to conservation will result and that October 1978 will stand as a climacteric in the evolution of their own awareness.

The action of the Secretary of State for Scotland

Mr Bruce Millan is to be applauded for his decision to call off the cull by the Norwegian sealing crew as soon as it became really apparent that there was a risk to human life. Greenpeace had made a reasonable request for a one-year moratorium and having been turned down it was clear that they meant business. With hindsight it might have been better to offer a compromise earlier in the proceedings, but one is aware of the risk of setting damaging precedents for the future. All in all, Mr Millan's gentlemanly concession to the weight of public concern was one of the most graceful climb-downs he could have achieved. His was an unenviable figurehead position, and the fault of the inadequate public relations and bad handling lies with his staff and advisers rather than on the individual whose training and experience are unlikely to have covered the subtleties of seal biology.

The aftermath

We were left with a pup cull to be effected by local, licensed pup hunters. Although this form of culling has been employed in the Orkneys for fifteen years it is known to have a limited result beyond the support of the seal-skin trade. It is not recommended as a method of population control and the levels fixed in the past have done nothing to check the expansion of the colonies. As a long-term policy it is clearly inferior to a combined adult and pup cull as proposed by the six-year plan. It is also slightly ironical that the animal welfare groups should have fought so tenaciously to remove the more humane cull system, to be left with the method which has the least desirable record.

The future

There is little doubt that seal controversy will rise again in Britain in the years ahead. The need for control will see to that and the government will have a difficult task if they are to please everyone.

It seems that a pelagic cull, out of the public eye, is likely to be investigated even if it is not adopted. It would certainly have some advantages in the political field as well as providing a greater opportunity to assemble data on grey seal feeding habits. In many ways the concept of a British sealing vessel constantly cruising round removing seals, although costly, might be better for seals and for science.

As far as the administration is concerned it is to be hoped that the same mistakes will not be made again. The proper dissemination of a management policy and its scientific support is essential from now on if the exercise is to proceed at all.

The conservation movement, too, should be seen to be as concerned about fish stocks as it has about seals. In many ways fish are more important because they are at a lower level in the pyramid of the ecosystem. It is no good protecting deer if there is no grass for them to eat. It is also as important that its opposition should be scientifically and rationally aligned, as should any new culling programme.

Appendix 1

PRESS RELEASES RELEVANT TO THE 1978 CONTROVERSY

(*Additional press releases appear in the text on pages 62–6 and 68–70*)

Press release issued on behalf of the Department of Agriculture and Fisheries for Scotland, 6 July 1978

A further cull of grey seals will take place this autumn in the breeding assemblies of Orkney, the North Rona National Nature Reserve and the Western Isles.

Mr Bruce Millan MP, Secretary of State for Scotland, has announced his decision to go ahead with the cull which is planned in accordance with a co-ordinated plan drawn up in 1977 for the years 1977 to 1982, on the advice of the Seals Advisory Committee of the Natural Environment Research Council (NERC).

Licences for shooting with approved fire-arms will be issued for a total cull of 900 adult breeding females and their associated pups and 4,000 moulted pups of which 450 adults will be taken in Orkney and 450 adults and 500 moulted pups in North Rona by the Norwegian firm of G. C. Rieber, who are being engaged on a contract by the Secretary of State. The remainder of the moulted pups will be taken by local hunters from Orkney and the Western Isles.

The Secretary of State's decision has been taken in accordance with his statutory reponsibilities under the Conservation of Seals Act 1970 for purposes of population management and prevention of damage to fisheries. He has consulted with NERC and has taken into account information on the size and distribution of the grey seal population in Scottish waters from the Sea Mammal Research Unit of NERC and the extent of predation of fish as estimated by fisheries scientists of the Department of Agriculture and Fisheries for Scotland. He also acknowledges the co-operation of the Nature Conservancy Council (NCC) with regard to the decision to cull on the North Rona National Nature Reserve as part of the co-ordinated plan.

Regular and systematic counts carried out by the Sea Mammal Research Unit (SMRU) since the 1960s confirm that there has been a rapid and large increase in the grey seal population in Scottish waters from about 35,000 in the mid-1960s to about 60,000 now.

Damage caused by grey seals to fisheries is considerable though difficult to estimate precisely because of the assumptions which need to be made. Seals live largely on fish suitable for human consumption and are in this respect in direct competition with man as consumers of valuable food supplies. The tonnage taken is estimated at between 5 per cent and 10 per cent of the total catch taken in the UK extended fishery limits and has been valued at over £12m.

To deal with this situation adequately in a manner which will substantially reduce the loss to fisheries, Government policy is to reduce seal numbers to the level of the mid-1960s, by approximately one half. To achieve this objective reasonably quickly the advice of the SMRU is that the best method is to cull 900 adult breeding females and 4,000 moulted pups per year during the six years 1977–82.

This advice takes account of the known facts about the life and habits of the grey seal, chiefly that a female grey seal can live for up to thirty-five years and may breed for up to twenty-eight years and that pup culling alone on past levels is insufficient to bring about a sufficient population reduction quickly. Pup culling at greatly increased levels would involve some risk to the future of the grey seal population.

The co-ordinated plan is based on proportional culling of all the main breeding assemblies which will provide more scientific information and enable life tables to be prepared upon which to base the long-term conservation and management of the grey seal. It is this aspect which particularly concerns the NCC.

The Secretary of State said: 'I recognize that many people throughout the country hold strong views on the subject of seal culling. However, I hope that all concerned will recognize that I am responsible for exercising statutory responsibilities, and I am satisfied on the evidence that action is necessary.'

Notes for Editors

1. *Conservation of Seals Act 1970.* Culling of grey seals is carried out under the provisions of the Conservation of Seals Act 1970. The Act provides for a close season for grey seals during the period from 1 September to 31 December, both dates inclusive, in order to protect grey seals during the breeding season when they are vulnerable. The Act also prohibits the killing or taking of any seal by the use of poison or by shooting other than with a rifle using ammunition having a muzzle energy of not less than 600 foot pounds and a bullet weighing not less than 45 grains. Under Section 10(1)(c) the Secretary of State may license any person to kill seals during the close season for:

(i) the prevention of damage to fisheries;
(ii) the reduction of a population surplus of seals for management purposes; or
(iii) the use of a population surplus of seals as a resource.

The Secretary of State is required to consult the Natural Environment Research Council (NERC) before granting any licence under this Act and, except in relation to the prevention of damage to fisheries, shall not without the consent of the Nature Conservancy Council grant a licence to kill or take seals in a nature reserve within the meaning of Section 15 of the National Parks and Access to the Countryside Act 1949 or in any area which has been notified as a site of special scientific interest under Section 23 of that Act.

Section 11 of the Act empowers the Secretary of State to authorize compulsory entry on to land by any person licensed to kill or take seals for the purpose of preventing damage to fisheries by seals, provided the requisite statutory notice is duly served. If any person wilfully obstructs any person so authorized by the Secretary of State to exercise entry under this section, he shall be guilty of an offence.

2. *Seals Advisory Committee.* The Seals Advisory Committee is an inter-Departmental committee set up by NERC in pursuance of the duty laid upon it under Section 13 of the Act to provide the Secretary of State with scientific advice on matters related to the management of seal populations. The Committee, under the Chairmanship of the Earl of Cranbrook, includes representation from NERC, including the Council's Sea Mammal Research Unit, NCC, DAFS and other Government Departments. The Committee maintains a close continuing oversight on all matters connected with the Act and, in particular, has approved a six-year management plan formulated on the advice of the SMRU. The Committee has also accepted the evidence presented by DAFS fisheries scientists on the extent of grey seal damage to fisheries.

3. *Sea Mammal Research Unit (SMRU).* This is a specialist research unit set up by NERC charged with the duties of studying and making recommendations on seal populations. The grey seal population of the British Isles has been studied by this unit, which has accumulated a very valuable and highly respected body of knowledge about the animal. Given the need to reduce the overall Scottish population by about one half, the advice of the unit is that its proposals provide the best and safest plan for achieving this result; in particular, taking full account of the future survival of the species. The unit also expects to obtain

valuable scientific information from the cull which should enable it to make future recommendations concerning long-term management of the grey seal population at the optimum level for both conservation of the species and minimizing damage to fisheries.

4. *Management plan.* The agreed management plan, based on a population model constructed by the S M R U, provides for the culling of 900 adult breeding females per year for six years, alternately in the Western Isles and Orkney and North Rona, and an annual pup cull of 4,000 moulted pups. This plan should achieve the required population reduction by 1982 if the target figures are achieved. To achieve the same result, relying purely on culling of moulted pups, would involve a massive increase in pup culling for several years. This would involve some risk to the future stability of the grey seal population.

5. *Fisheries damage.* The estimates of the total loss to fisheries as a result of grey seal predation, assessed by the scientists of the D A F S Marine Laboratory, are based on known evidence although they involve a number of broad assumptions which have to be made. Starting from the position that the average consumption of each individual seal is estimated at about 15 lb. of fish or other foods per day, and that the total population around the Scottish coast is now reasonably well known, it is estimated that grey seals take 168,000 tonnes of fish or other sea animals. An allowance is made that about 30 per cent of the seal diet will be drawn from invertebrates such as molluscs and crustacea, leaving about 130,000 tonnes of fish normally exploited for human consumption which comprises the remainder of the seals' diet. Given an average annual rate of exploitation of 50 per cent by the fishing industry it is estimated that 56,000 tonnes of fish which would otherwise be caught for human consumption is eaten by grey seals. This tonnage can be expressed as between 5 and 10 per cent to the total catch taken within the UK's extended fishery limit of 200 miles and has been valued at over £12m. While not very much is known about the range of distribution of grey seals at sea, it is well known that seals do feed on salmon in coastal waters, particularly in the vicinity of salmon netting stations where they cause significant damage, and on other commercially important fish species.

6. *Seal culling.* This is a difficult job carried out at some risk to the licensee. It has to be carried out at a time of year when weather conditions in the remote islands off the Western Isles and in Orkney can be

very unfavourable. It is a difficult and unpleasant job and the return to the participants depends on securing a reasonable market for pup skins. Adult culling is more difficult; each adult carcase may weigh up to 3 and 5 cwts for cows and bulls respectively and handling involves heavy tackle and hard work. A successful adult cull requires careful planning and organization with the minimum prior disturbance of the colonies. Any disturbance prior to the cull leads to the animals leaving the breeding beaches prematurely to try to find other breeding locations.

7. *Ferne animal sanctuary*. The island of Little Linga owned by this registered charity is included amongst the Orkney breeding sites to be culled. The island has no status in law as a sanctuary and the statutory provisions of the 1970 Act apply as to any other island in private ownership. The estimated population of Little Linga based on regular counts of pups born has more than doubled since the mid-1960s, and there is no case for excluding it from the co-ordinated plan which was designed to cover the full range of breeding assemblies including those on National Nature Reserves.

8. *Common seals*. In addition to grey seals there are around 11,000 common seals (*Phoca vitulina*) which breed on sandbanks in Scottish waters and which are protected by the Conservation of Seals Act 1970. The close season for these is from 1 June to 31 August. Some culling of common seal pups is permitted under licence during the close season but there is no need for more control measures.

Press release issued by the Scottish Society for Prevention of Cruelty to Animals, 22 August 1978

The public in Orkney and elsewhere is very understandably concerned about the intention to cull 900 adult breeding female grey seals and their associated pups and 4,000 moulted pups in Orkney and North Rona this autumn. The reason is stated to be that it is necessary to conserve for human consumption fish which would otherwise be taken by an unacceptably high grey seal population. My Society is not convinced that grey seals do materially affect the numbers of fish, which must surely be reduced very much more by the feeding of the hundreds of thousands of seabirds round Northern shores. Indeed, many of the seals around Scotland appear to feed primarily on stocks of fish that are not harvested by man.

While its members are naturally interested in wildlife conservation, my Society's concern is for the welfare of all animals and birds, common as well as rare, ugly as well as beautiful: i.e. we exist to prevent suffering. Unfortunately, the killing of wild and domestic animals, rightly or wrongly, is practised daily for the feeding and clothing of man and my Society's duty is to see that such killing, whether it be directly or indirectly for the benefit of man, is carried out humanely.

The cull is part of a six-year programme to reduce the grey seal population by approximately one half, that is to the numbers which existed in the mid-1960s.

Licences for shooting with approved firearms will be issued to a Norwegian firm of sealers for the culling of 450 adult seals in Orkney and 540 adults and 500 moulted pups in North Rona. The remainder of the moulted pups will be taken by licensed local hunters from Orkney and the Western Isles.

Thus all the adult females and their pups will be taken by one firm. One of the Society's Inspectors was present throughout the similar cull in the Outer Hebrides last autumn, and he was satisfied that all the seals were killed with the first shot. In the same way pups were killed instantaneously.

The remaining problem is to minimize the suffering of the orphaned pups. It is not possible to tell immediately which pup has been orphaned and it is necessary to return to the beach later that day or the following day to see which pups are showing signs of not having been suckled by their mothers.

Without conceding that the operation is necessary in the first place, my Society is satisfied that the arrangements made involve a strictly limited amount of suffering on the part of these orphan pups.

My Society is, however, very concerned at the proposal of well-wishing people to demonstrate on the breeding beaches to try to prevent the cull from taking place. This will in itself cause suffering to the seals which are highly sensitive to human presence. Such continuing demonstrations would inevitably result in a complete disturbance of the local seal population, with the result that the cows would be driven to have their pups on probably less suitable parts of the shore, where mortality would almost certainly be higher than normal, and cows may abort. Demonstrating during actual culling operations, apart from the danger to public safety, will almost certainly lead to a much higher risk of cruelty to the seals through distraction of the marksmen and the movement of the animals. Demonstrators' presence after any shooting would prevent the remaining cows from suckling their pups.

My Society appeals to all those who at present plan to take part in a demonstration on the beaches to think better of it and to make their protests in some other way.

Press release issued by the Scottish Fishermen's Federation and the British Fishing Federation Ltd (Scottish Office), 20 September 1978

The Scottish Fishermen's Federation and the Scottish Office of the British Fishing Federation, which together represent substantially the interests of the owners of both inshore and deep sea fishing vessels operating from Scottish ports, have followed with interest – but so far with a reluctance to comment – the public debate which has been evoked as a result of the decision of the Secretary of State for Scotland to go ahead with the proposed cull of Grey Seals at Orkney, North Rona and the Western Isles as part of the co-ordinated plan drawn up in 1977.

The Fishing Federations have, however, now studied very carefully the scientific advice which has led the Secretary of State to authorizing a programme of seal culling over the years 1977/1982 and in particular have noted firstly, that the Grey Seal population in Scottish Waters has doubled since the mid-1960s and that, above all, it is estimated that 56,000 tonnes of fish per annum, which would otherwise be caught for human consumption, is eaten by Grey Seals.

Whilst we appreciate the sensitivity of the whole question of seal culling, and also respect the sincerity of the opinions held by those who oppose it, scientific facts clearly demonstrate that the substantially increased seal population is having a devastating effect on fish stocks – including some of the prime human consumption species – which are already under very severe pressure from all directions; indeed the fishing industry is currently suffering very painfully, in both human and economic terms, from the imposition of catch controls throughout all the areas in which it has traditionally operated and this is quite irreconcilable with a situation which permits a growing seal population to make such substantial inroads into valuable human-consumption fish stocks.

The Scottish Fishermen's Federation and the Scottish Office of the British Fishing Federation believe that the Secretary of State's six-year plan for the culling of Grey Seals, based on recommendations from the Seals Advisory Committee of the Natural Environment Research Council, has been devised in a genuine, objective and humane way with a view to striking the right balance between the respective conservation and management needs of the seal and commercial fisheries populations and consequently we think it right to make it known publicly at this time that we support the Secretary of State in his decision to proceed with the forthcoming 1978 cull as part of the overall plan.

Press release issued by the Scottish Office, 3 October 1978

Officials of the Department of Agriculture and Fisheries for Scotland met representatives of the Greenpeace Foundation in Edinburgh this afternoon to discuss the forthcoming seal cull.

After hearing the views of the Foundation, officials explained the circumstances in which the Secretary of State had decided to carry out a further cull of grey seals. Grey seals have been protected by legislation in this country since 1914. The present legislation prescribes certain circumstances in which licences may be granted for the killing of seals during the close season. Since statutory protection was first introduced the population of grey seals has increased substantially to about 60,000. It is estimated that the numbers have doubled in the past decade and are likely to continue to increase at this rate unless further control measures are taken. There are no known natural factors which are likely to stabilize the population. This year's adult cull of 900 breeding cows involves only $1\frac{1}{2}$ per cent of the total estimated population. Seals are known to live up to thirty-five years and may breed for twenty-eight years.

The resultant loss to fisheries from this level of population is considered to be very high. Although no precise assessment can be made, it is estimated that grey seals take between 5 and 10 per cent of the catchable fish in British waters, which at average landed prices is valued in the region of £12m.

It was explained to the Foundation's representatives that the Secretary of State's decision to carry out a further cull this year is based on the advice of the Seals Advisory Committee and was taken after consultation with the Natural Environment Research Council and the Nature Conservancy Council, both of which bodies will be co-operating in the cull as part of an integrated scientific programme. The Secretary of State is satisfied on the advice that he has been given that the action which is proposed will not put the future of the grey seal at any risk. The culling operation will be reviewed each year to take account of the results obtained.

Officials made it clear that there is no question of the cull being undertaken for commercial reasons or for the convenience of the fur trade. Adult seal skins are not valuable, the main trade being in the skins of moulted pups.

The culling contractor is being allowed to purchase the skins at agreed prices in order to reduce the public cost of the operation. The conduct of the operation and the activities of the contractor will be under direct control, and observers will be present to ensure that the terms of the licence are observed. Animal welfare interests will also be present to observe the cull.

Officials emphasized that the Secretary of State fully respects the views of those who have expressed concern about the future of the grey seal and has anxiously considered all the views that have been put to him in this respect before deciding whether to exercise his statutory responsibilities in this matter. He has, however, carefully reviewed the evidence that has been put to him and is satisfied that the action proposed is necessary. Since the Secretary of State's decision was announced on 6 July, there has been little serious questioning of the scientific basis of the decision.

It was pointed out to the representatives that it is of considerable importance that the operation should be carried out efficiently and humanely and with as little disturbance as possible. Any action which might cause any further disturbance to the seal colonies could lead to additional distress to the seals by increasing the number of abandoned pups.

Notes for Editors

The first Grey Seals Protection Act was passed in 1914 when the grey seal population around Britain was estimated at 500. This Act gave grey seals complete protection during their breeding season when the cows and pups are on land and are vulnerable. The Act of 1932 recognized the need to provide for some control of numbers and empowered Ministers to issue permits to kill seals with approved fire-arms during the closed season. The present Act passed in 1970 extended protection to the common seal during its breeding season and defined more precisely the purposes for which Ministers can grant licences to kill seals during the closed season as scientific research, the prevention of damage to fisheries, to reduce numbers for management purposes or exploitation of the seals as a resource. Where a Minister has powers granted by Parliament he would be failing in his duty if he refused to exercise them where he was satisfied that a sufficient case had been made.

In relation to the present culling programme the case presented to the Secretary of State was based on scientific evidence collected over a number of years by a specialist unit of the Natural Environment Research Council. This showed that grey seal numbers off the Scottish coast had doubled since the mid-1960s and could be expected to double again in the next ten years if no effective control action was taken. Evidence provided by the Director of Fisheries Research at the Department's Marine Laboratory estimated that the loss to the sea fisheries catch caused by grey seal predation at the present population level was of the order of 56,000 tonnes annually which represents 5 to 10 per cent of the catch in the British waters out to 200 miles and costs at average landed prices over £12m.

The culling programme submitted to the Secretary of State in 1977 with the approval of the Seals Advisory Committee was a plan for controlled culling of adult cows and pups at the main breeding assemblies over six years designed to reduce this part of the grey seal population in Scottish waters to the level of the mid-1960s, i.e. by about one half, the principal aim was to reduce the loss to fisheries, but the plan was conceived to provide sufficient scientific samples to enable a well-based control and conservation policy to be evolved for the future.

The present year's cull is not being undertaken for commercial reasons or for the convenience of the fur trade. Adult seal skins are not valuable; the trade is in skins of moulted pups. On scientific advice the Seals Advisory Committee decided that increased culling of moulted pups on the scale needed to reduce the population would involve some risk to the future of the animals. This is why the culling of adults was decided upon. In order to reduce the cost to public funds any value in the skins and carcasses should be realized and arrangements have been made for a contractor to buy the skins at agreed prices. The net cost to the Government will however be between £10,000 and £20,000 depending on how many seals are taken. The price of a top-quality moulted pup skin is no more than £10.

The operation is to be carried out by the Norwegian company, G. C. Rieber. The reason for engaging this company on a two-year contract in 1977 was that no British firm could offer to provide for the accommodation of scientific and official observers who are needed to fulfil both purposes of the operation. There will be no killing of seals other than by approved fire-arms.

Responsible conservationists recognize that complete protection of any species is not necessarily desirable; control may be needed particularly where a species is not subject to control by natural predators. Control of the grey seal population is clearly necessary. The Nature Conservancy Council are co-operating in the cull as part of an integrated scientific programme to enable a long-term management policy for the entire population of grey seals to be developed.

There is no question of the future of the grey seal population being at risk. The cull plan has been carefully conceived to bring about a controlled reduction over several years in the grey seal population and the strict supervision of each stage is to ensure that the plan is adhered to. Moreover the plan can be adjusted from year to year in the light of experience.

Despite reports that fishermen do not support the need for action, both the Scottish Fishermen's Federation and the British Fishing Federation have gone firmly on record in support of the cull.

Press release issued by the Scottish Office, 6 October 1978

Secretary of State replies to comments by Mr Jo Grimond

Mr Bruce Millan, M P, Secretary of State for Scotland, has written to The Rt Hon. Jo Grimond, M P, in answer to letters sent to him on 19 and 26 September regarding the forthcoming seal cull in the Orkney Islands.

The full text of the Secretary of State's reply is as follows:

'You wrote to me on 19 and 26 September regarding the public meeting in Orkney about the grey seal cull which was addressed by Lord Cranbrook and others.

'I have seen a report of this meeting and it seems to me that a good deal of effort was made to explain the facts and the background to my decision. I would suppose, however, that many of the people present were opposed to seal culling as a matter of conviction and were not likely to change their opinion whatever information they were given.

'What is important is that we should look at the facts available to us. These are that the grey seal population in our waters has increased very substantially since statutory protection was introduced in 1914, and from our knowledge of the animal and its habits this increase will certainly continue at a significant rate if there is no control action, and will not be arrested if control is limited to the hunting of moulted pups at the levels allowed in recent years. There is no evidence that natural factors are likely to stabilize or reduce the numbers in the foreseeable future.

'I understand that the Orkney Islands Council rejected a motion last week proposing that they should protest about the cull. I assume that you will also have seen or heard of the views recently put out by the Scottish Fishermen's Federation and the British Fishermen's Federation in support of the proposed cull. I understand that the local Orkney fishermen's organization shares these views. There is no doubt that the opinion that seals do not damage fisheries is in conflict with both the scientific evidence and with the views of the fishermen.

'Without wanting to repeat what I have already told you, the loss to fisheries is very high and, despite deficiencies in the known facts about the seal diet, the quantification by my Director of Fisheries Research is the best evidence available. I have seen no serious challenge to it. My replies to the questions put to me on 20 February and 26 July do not seem to me to be in conflict with this or with each other. The first of these was directed to a specific question about salmon in a limited context and the figures were calculated on assumptions which would not have been appropriate to the more general question which I answered on 26 July. As you will be aware, although fish constitute the main component of the seal's diet, it also includes invertebrates. Clearly what is important is the total damage being caused to fish stocks suitable for human consumption and not to particular species.

'As to the organization and cost of the operation, given the need to combine a scientific sampling exercise with the culling operation, it is necessary for the vessel to have accommodation for scientists and observers. The function of the observers is to ensure that the strict conditions of the licence are carried out. The Norwegian company of G. C. Rieber are able to meet our requirements in this respect. They were engaged on contract in 1977 for two years on the basis of an agreed daily charter fee with an offsetting allowance for the skins taken.

'The net cost will not be known until the operation is completed but it is expected to be in the region of £15,000–£20,000. I assume that the terms of the contract will cover Rieber's costs, but that is their concern. I am satisfied for my part that the cull is being carried out on the best terms available. My information is that the pelts will be sold at prevailing market prices, which I think you will find are nowhere near £30 per skin as you suggest.

'In announcing my decision that the proposed cull would go ahead this year, I said that I hoped that the many people who hold understandably strong views on the subject of grey seals would accept that the action proposed was necessary. From the protests which have been made, both to me and publicly, some people still do not accept this. Let me therefore make my own position clear.

'I respect the view of those who think that animals should not be killed in any circumstances, whether for food or to prevent damage to our economy or environment. I do not think, however, that most other people, who are just as concerned about the welfare of grey seals and other wild animals, share this view. They accept that man's economic need and the needs of the species itself may sometimes justify the killing of certain animals, each case requiring to be considered on its merits. The grey seal population has doubled over the last decade or so, and is likely to go on increasing if control is only by means of pup hunting carried out under licence.

'I am advised that in these circumstances the loss to fisheries is much too high, being put at between 5 and 10 per cent per annum of the catchable fish in British waters and valued at over £12m. You yourself have on many occasions in other contexts expressed concern for the future of local fisheries and fishing communities. Accordingly I have accepted the scientific advice that a cull of adult seals should be carried out on a systematic basis over a period of years. The adult cows to be culled constitute about $1\frac{1}{2}$ per cent per year of the present *adult* population. I am assured that such a reduction will not put the future of the grey seal population at any risk, and in any event the culling plans are subject to review from year to year.

'Finally I am concerned about reports that some people from Orkney and elsewhere plan to take disruptive action, including landing on the seal islands to disturb the colonies. This is likely to be harmful to the seals, and moreover could involve some risk to the persons involved. The officers in charge of the cull will be instructed to respect the rights of persons to make peaceful protest within the law, and to take no action likely to put human life at risk. I hope, however, that any other persons and organizations who have it in mind to be in the vicinity will not be encouraged to hazard their lives by attempting to land on rocky islands from small boats in possibly adverse conditions.

'I note that you would like to bring a deputation to see me later next week. I would, of course, be happy to meet you and I am asking my office to get in touch with you to arrange this. I should say now, however, that the arrangements for this year's cull, which I announced as far back as 6 July, are now complete and I have authorized the operation to go ahead.

'I am sure that you will agree that in view of the public interest in this matter, I should make this reply available to the Press.'

Press release issued by the Scottish Office, 9 October 1978

This material has been compiled as a background note on this autumn's cull of grey seals in Orkney, North Rona and the Western Isles.

Systematic counts by the Sea Mammal Research Unit of the Natural Environment Research Council (N E R C) since 1960s confirm approximate doubling in the grey seal population in Scottish waters to about 60,000 now.

This year's cull is the second of a six-year co-ordinated programme drawn up in 1977 on the advice of the Seals Advisory Committee of NERC to reduce the grey seal population to the level of the mid-sixties. Cull figures for this year total 900 adult breeding females and their associated pups and 4,000 moulted pups. The adult cows to be culled in 1978 represent about 1½ per cent of the present *adult* population. While the principal aim is to reduce the loss of fisheries, the plan was conceived to provide sufficient scientific samples to enable a well-based control and conservation policy to be evolved for the future.

The world's grey seal population is estimated to be in the region of 110,000. The reduction proposed will not put the future of the population of the species at any risk and in any event the culling plans will be reviewed from year to year.

The Secretary of State has engaged the Norwegian firm of G. C. Rieber who will cull 450 adults in Orkney and 450 adults and 500 moulted pups in North Rona. The culling of adult seals is a specialist job and one which local hunters are not equipped to carry out. Local hunters who traditionally cull in Orkney and the Western Isles will take the remainder of the moulted pups in these breeding areas.

The estimates of the total loss to fisheries as a result of grey seal predation, assessed by the scientists of the DAFS Marine Laboratory, are based on known evidence which is corroborated by work done in other countries. From the position that the average consumption of each individual seal is estimated at about 15 lb. of fish or other foods per day, and that the total population around the Scottish coast is now reasonably well known, it is estimated that grey seals take 168,000 tonnes of fish or other sea animals. An allowance is made that about 30 per cent of the seal diet will consist of species of fish and invertebrates of non-commercial importance, leaving about 130,000 tonnes of fish normally exploited for human consumption which comprises the remainder of the seals' diet. Using a conservative figure of 50 per cent for the average annual rate of exploitation by the fishing industry it is estimated that some 56,000 tonnes of fish which would otherwise be caught for human consumption is eaten by grey seals. This tonnage can be expressed as between 5 and 10 per cent of the total catch taken within the UK's extended fishery limit of 200 miles and has been valued at over £12m. These statistics are based on information gathered during the period 1959–75.

Cost of the cull will not be known until the operation is completed but it is expected to be in the region of £15,000–£20,000. Rieber will be paid a contractual fee and will in turn pay a purchase price to the Department for the skins taken. Local hunters do not receive any payment from the Department and cover costs by what they can get for the pelts.

The skins of adult seals are of little value and information available puts the market price for a top-quality moulted pup pelt at £10 – nowhere near the £30 per skin as has been suggested. There is no question of the cull being undertaken for commercial reasons or for the convenience of the fur trade. Adult seal skins are not valuable, the main trade being in the skins of moulted pups.

Press release issued by the Scottish Society for the Prevention of Cruelty to Animals, 10 October 1978

The Scottish SPCA appeals again to protestors against the present grey seal cull in the North of Scotland not themselves to go on to the breeding beaches. Reports indicate that already, before the cull has even begun, colonies have been disturbed and many cows have abandoned their pups, which are now starving to death. This afternoon there have even been reports of some cows returning to their pups and rolling on them. The suffering of these pups has been caused not by those licensed to carry out the cull but by those who are trying to prevent it taking place.

The Scottish SPCA is not convinced that there is sufficient evidence of damage to domestic fishery stocks to justify a cull, but it is an established fact that the Scottish grey seal population has doubled since the mid-1960s, and this may be partly due to the degree of protection which these animals have had under British law.

The Society's concern is to see that the cull is carried out humanely and that any suffering to orphaned pups is kept to the minimum. With this object it has one Inspector at sea, who will accompany the marksmen, and others on the beaches who will try to ensure after the cull that orphaned pups are killed humanely as quickly as they can be identified.

It would be ironic and very sad if those who disagree so strongly with the cull, presumably on humanitarian grounds for the species is not in danger of extinction, were to be responsible for much unnecessary suffering.

Press release issued by the Scottish Office, 16 October 1978

Mr Bruce Millan, MP, Secretary of State for Scotland, has reaffirmed the Government's long-term policy regarding the culling of grey seals in the Orkneys and the Western Isles, but has announced a reduction in this year's cull.

In a statement issued today, Mr Millan said: 'I have now reviewed the situation regarding this cull. I reaffirm the Government's long-term policy in this matter. The management plan which I am following was recommended to me by the Seals Advisory Committee which is widely representative and includes members of the Nature Conservancy Council, the Natural Environment Research Council, Universities and other bodies. They have recommended this plan in the light of the substantial increase in the population of grey seals, and it is their view that the present increase is likely to continue. I welcome the statements made by both the NCC and the NERC supporting the management plan.

'The Seals Advisory Committee has been examining the problem of the increasing number of grey seals for some seven years. None of the discussions which I have had over the past week with conservationist interests has produced any evidence to contradict the advice which I have had from the Committee and from my own scientists.

'Research has been undertaken over many years into seal behaviour, diet etc. and there is no doubt that they are consuming considerable quantities of fish which has been put at a value of some £12m per annum. The simple facts of the matter are that seals eat fish as their main diet, mostly fish suitable for human consumption, and the more seals there are, the greater the damage done to the fish stocks. I am bound, as Secretary of State, to have regard in this situation to the interests of both the consumer and the fishermen whose livelihoods are at stake.

'I am also anxious to ensure that the future of the species is not endangered but there is absolutely no question of that being at issue, as the NCC and the NERC have confirmed.

'The advice I have had from the Seals Advisory Committee is that given the present level of the grey seal population, unless some reductions is made in the number of adults, there would have to be a very considerable increase in the level of pup culling to achieve the necessary reduction in the total stock. This increased pup culling could result in a serious upsetting of the balance of the population.

'There has been considerable attention given to the presence of a Norwegian firm in this operation. I wish to point out that the Norwegian firm is, in the main, being employed for only one part of the operation – the culling of adult seals – and this is solely because there are no local hunters equipped to do this part of the operation. If adult culling is not carried out, the need for pup culling will increase.

'The major part of the pup culling has been planned to be carried out by local hunters. Licences have been issued annually for this purpose since 1962.

'Although I believe that the scientific advice which I have been given is correct, and that the cull as envisaged in the management plan recommended by the Seals Advisory Committee should be carried out, I am conscious of the widespread public concern which exists. I have decided therefore to reduce the size of the cull this year so that everyone will have the opportunity to study the scientific evidence and to submit to me for evaluation other data which they may have available. I must stress that so far such evidence from the objectors has been absent.

'In the light of this situation and notwithstanding what I have said about the need for an adult cull, I have decided to withdraw the Norwegian firm.

'I have also decided to restrict the pup cull. In earlier years, the level of the pup cull has varied between 750 and 2,000 (in 1975). I propose that this year's pup cull in the Orkneys and the Western Isles should be at this latter level. This will mean that the management plan which has been recommended to me will require to be revised.

'I have already given an undertaking to the conservation interests that I will make public all the scientific evidence available, so that anyone who believes that better scientific data exists can submit it to me for evaluation.

'I will also ask the Seals Advisory Committee, and my own scientists, to consider any such evidence and to publish their conclusions in good time before next year's cull. At the end of the day, the policy decision must be mine, but I will consider any relevant views which are put to me.'

Press release issued by the National Environment Research Council, 16 October 1978

The Natural Environment Research Council (NERC) wishes to make the following statement concerning the facts relating to the cull of grey seals in the Orkneys.

The total number of grey seals around the coasts of Britain is in the region of seventy thousand. The majority live in the waters to the north and west of Scotland, where in recent years they have been increasing at an annual rate of 7 per cent. If this rate of increase continues, their numbers will have doubled in little more than ten years' time. There are no obvious natural checks in this region to a population increase of this magnitude.

Fish comprise the main diet of grey seals. A seal population as large as that in British waters needs to consume between one and two hundred thousand tons of fish annually to sustain itself.

Precise figures for the total direct loss to the commercial fisheries caused by seals are impossible to obtain, except in the case of salmon and salmon gear. However, from observations of the eating habits of seals, even the most conservative estimate is that many thousands of tons of commercially valuable fish that would otherwise have been caught are eaten annually by seals. In money terms, this represents a loss to the fishermen of many millions of pounds each year. There is every reason to believe that if the seal stocks increase so will the damage they cause to the fisheries.

In these circumstances, the Department of Agriculture and Fisheries for Scotland decided that management of the seal stocks should be undertaken in order to give a degree of protection to the commercial fisheries. In accordance with the provisions of the Conservation of Seals Act, 1970, the Department sought the advice of the NERC on how the seal stocks could be controlled to achieve this objective. Among the criteria were that the strictest humane standards should be observed and that there should be no danger to the future viability of the seal stocks.

On the basis of the scientific and practical knowledge of seal populations obtained over many years by the staff of the NERC Seal Mammal Research Unit and other scientists elsewhere, the NERC recommended that the Department's requirements could be met by the culling regime which is proposed.

This regime, which was also discussed with and approved by the Seals Advisory Committee on which various interests including the Nature Conservancy Council are represented, has the following objectives for control of the seal populations:

(a) in the first instance, to arrest the present increasing trend in seal numbers
(b) eventually, to bring the seal populations in Scottish waters to an equilibrium state some 15,000 less than at present.

A more detailed account of the culling regime is given in a statement issued today by the NERC Sea Mammal Research Unit.

This new equilibrium, which would not be reached for some years, would mean a decrease of between 15 per cent and 20 per cent in the total British population of grey seals. Such a decrease would in no way threaten the viability of the seal stocks. Moreover, the resulting numbers would still be above those which the former Consultative Committee on Grey Seals and Fisheries regarded in 1963 as undesirably high from the point of view of the fisheries.

Continuous monitoring and research will be undertaken by the staff of the NERC Sea Mammal Research Unit to measure the effect of culling and changes in the seal stocks. The results will be published regularly and should there be any indication that changes were not following the expected pattern, the evidence would be made known at once so that remedial action could be taken.

In view of the controversy that has arisen, it is necessary to make clear that the present cull, which has been authorized by the Secretary of State for Scotland, is consistent with the scientific advice provided by the NERC in accordance with its statutory responsibilities. That advice is based on research on British seals the results of which have been published on numerous occasions in the scientific literature and elsewhere. Those results are widely acknowledged by scientists in this and other countries as providing an essentially correct picture of the stocks of British seals and of changes in them.

Press release issued by the Council for Nature's Grey Seal Group, 26 October 1978

The Council for Nature's Grey Seal Group was formed this afternoon at a meeting of the Fauna Preservation Society, Greenpeace, People's Trust for Endangered Species, the Society for the Promotion of Nature Conservation and the World Wildlife Fund, all conservation organizations which are opposed to the recently abandoned Orkney/North Rona Cull. The Mammal Society, which is also anxious that the data is objectively assessed, attended as an observer, and at future meetings an observer from the International Union for Conservation of Nature will be invited.

The meeting was held in order to assess the existing data on the role of grey seals in their ecosystem and especially their impact on commercial fisheries. This was in response to the Secretary of State for Scotland's agreement to make available all the data upon which his decision had been made and to consider further representations before another cull is agreed. A researcher is being engaged immediately on behalf of the Group to enable the group to assess the data used by DAFS in formulating their policy. All other available data will be considered and proposals for future research will be made.

Appendix 2

A PERSONAL STATEMENT BY LORD CRANBROOK, CHAIRMAN OF THE SEALS ADVISORY COMMITTEE, SEPTEMBER 1978

Grey seals management

Parliament has always been conscious of the fact that seals can do harm to fisheries and has legislated accordingly.

Though it was said by the Board of Agriculture and Fisheries that seals were not then an important factor so far as fisheries were concerned, the Grey Seals Protection Act 1914, giving them complete protection during their breeding season, was only to last for five years since it was realized that the situation could change under protection.

The Act, though, was continued from year to year until it was realized that some control might be necessary and the Grey Seals Protection Act 1932 gave the Minister power to issue permits to kill them during the breeding season.

It was under that Act that the Minister authorized an annual pup cull in Orkney which was intended to reduce the 1963 population of 10,500 by 25 per cent over the next few years.

That was done after some extensive research by the Nature Conservancy and on the advice of a 'Consultative Committee on Grey Seals and Fisheries' set up in 1959 (Appendix 3).

The Conservation of Seals Act 1970 gives protection during their breeding seasons to common as well as grey seals and follows the 1932 Act in giving the Minister power to control the population of both by giving licences to kill in specified areas during the breeding season, but added the power to give complete all-the-year-round protection where necessary. Under the Act NERC has the duty of advising the Minister on the management of seal populations and has set up a Seals Research Division and a Seals Advisory Committee to enable it to do so.

In spite of the annual cull authorized in 1963 and still continuing, the Orkney breeding population had grown to 12,500 by 1973 and to 14,500 in 1977.

Research has shown that though the English Farne Island population is probably a discrete breeding unit there is a considerable interchange of individuals between the Hebrides, Orkney and North Rona and the whole Scottish population must be regarded as a single breeding unit.

That Scottish population has grown from an estimated 29,500 in 1963 to 54,000 in 1973 and 60,000+ in 1977. It has doubled over the last eleven years and will probably double again over the next eleven.

It is not likely that the number of seals will ever be controlled by lack of fish in the sea to eat and though the perinatal death rate increases with overcrowding on the breeding sites there are no signs of that becoming a significant factor in the foreseeable future. On the Farnes that overcrowding is destroying the environment though the population has continued to grow. Grey seals have no enemies save man and killer whales, the latter relatively uncommon in British waters.

Some damage by seals to nets and fisheries is a normal occupational hazard and accepted as such by fishermen but, if excessive, can damage a man's livelihood and become unsupportable, though the breaking point is difficult to define.

It can be recognized in inshore drift-net fishing, now only practised in a few areas, and in inshore fixed-net fishing for salmon, though there it seems to have stabilized at a disturbing level which can be regarded as supportable. There does though seem to be an increase in the number of salmon taken or injured at sea as those coming injured into dragnets seem to be increasing.

The main loss to fisheries is now the increased loss from seal predation at sea, which can only be quantified and that only very roughly by knowing the total number of seals, the average daily consumption and a knowledge of the species taken, found by examination of stomach contents.

The total annual consumption by seals is something of the nature of 170,000 tons, of which two-thirds will be fish, half of them or one-third of the total of commercially valuable species, between 5 and 10 per cent of the total catch in Scottish waters. The moment at which that loss becomes serious is obviously difficult to determine. The Consultative Committee of 1959 thought that the danger point had been reached by 1963. The existing Advisory Committee has watched the Scottish grey seal population grow, in Orkney in spite of an annual cull, until it is double that of 1963 and decided that the time had come to reverse the process by an additional annual cull of 900 adult females and their associated pups over each of the six years 1977 to 1982.

That cull is to be in the Hebrides and in Orkney with North Rona in alternate years.

Outside Scotland the National Trust has plans to maintain the population on the Farnes at a level which should not do damage to the environment and grey seals remain protected in Wales and south-west England. There are not enough breeding sites to allow that last group to increase to any great extent.

The main point at issue is the amount of fish eaten by seals at sea. That means the daily consumption by the average seal by weight and species × total number. Present knowledge of the first is based on examination of stomach contents and known amounts fed to captive ones. What is needed is the examination of many more stomachs and the six-year cull would of course produce a gradually increasing amount of knowledge on food consumption.

Appendix 3

RECOMMENDATIONS OF THE CONSULTATIVE COMMITTEE ON GREY SEALS AND FISHERIES, 1963
(Published by the Nature Conservancy and HMSO)

Recommendations for management and control of grey seals in Great Britain and for reducing the damage which they cause to fisheries

On the basis of findings which are summarized in sections 1–9 of this Report, the scientific, economic and humane considerations can be balanced into a general policy of research on British grey seal stocks and their management and control during the next five years. In establishing the policy the main considerations are as follows:

(i) The grey seal is an uncommon species of which at least two-thirds of those in the world breed around northern Britain. In that area, most breeding colonies are densely populated and the seals are thriving and probably increasing in numbers. Certain of the colonies are so active that they offer the possibility of harvesting seals as a resource, and could suffer a significant reduction of their numbers without in any way endangering the species as a whole.

(ii) It is well established that the local effect of large numbers of seals is deleterious to fisheries on account of the damage to fishing gear and to fish-catch, direct predation and as vectors of worm parasites. In certain areas, and in certain types of fishery, notably in the salmon fishery along the coast of Scotland, seals are of real significance in the economics of the industry. This applies also in certain areas to the white-fish industry, but as much in relation to the infestation by cod-worm as in the direct damage to fish or catch. The Committee has assessed the damage occasioned by seals and has considered methods by which it can be reduced.

(iii) The two colonies from which emanate the great majority of seals which affect the critical area of the east coast of Scotland are those of the Orkney Islands and the Farne Islands. A series of trial culling operations undertaken during 1960 and 1961 on the Orkney Islands has demonstrated methods by which seals can be killed during the breeding season without causing any cruelty and without undue disturbance to the breeding colonies.

(iv) So far as salmon fisheries are concerned the most obvious place for protective measure is at the nets, either by destroying seals or by modifying the materials and construction of the nets so as to reduce the damage to them. Salmon fishermen commonly use rifles in the vicinity of their nets, but the grey seal is a wily and intelligent animal, it presents a very poor target and is seldom shot. Rifle fire does, however, scare them and is primarily useful for that purpose. It is ineffective at night and in conditions of poor visibility. We are satisfied that by itself the method is by no means adequate to achieve any sizeable effect of protection. In the construction of nets artificial fibres have come into use in recent years and nets have been modified, e.g. by insertion of gussets in the fishcourts, to make it more difficult for seals to prey on the fish in them, and to prevent the nets being torn by seals escaping from them. When they have been applied these measures appear to have reduced net damage considerably, but they can have no effect on predation outside the nets nor on the problems of those who use other kinds of fishing gear.

(v) The Committee is satisfied that, neither by themselves nor together, are these two methods of control adequate. Therefore the Committee has had to consider action at the breeding colonies themselves, and has concluded that an experimental control should be attempted in the interest of fisheries; it might well be that such control would prove to be for the benefit of the colonies as well.

The Committee accordingly make the following recommendations:

1. Further studies should continue on the distribution, population structure and general biology of grey seals, and in particular on changes in the population which may be related to the measures on control recommended below. Investigations should continue also on the utilization of products from the seals killed in the control operations.

2. Every opportunity should be taken to speed up the replacement of traditional materials by new artificial fibres in the construction of nets, in order to reduce the amount of damage by seals; and also to destroy or scare seals near the nets by rifle fire.

3. A policy of control of numbers, and, where feasible, of harvesting the crop of seals, should be applied to the two colonies of the Orkneys and Farnes. In both cases the killing of seals on the breeding grounds should be arranged so as to reduce the breeding potential by about one-quarter (to 75 per cent of the present breeding potential) and the operation should be spread over five years. Detailed procedures recommended are stated below. In making this recommendation the Committee recognizes that the operations must be experimental in the sense that

the effect on fisheries of these measures cannot be predicted with precision.

4. It is essential, therefore, as part of the measures recommended for the control of seal numbers, that plans be made to assess the results of reducing the breeding population not only in terms of the seal populations themselves, but also in terms of the fisheries. For the latter to be possible, it will be necessary to develop the methods of obtaining information and statistical data regarding the damage done by seals (a) to salmon nets (both conventional nets and those made of synthetic fibre) and (b) to salmon, especially salmon catches. This information must be so standardized as to provide from 1963 onwards reasonably comparable information from year to year throughout the experimental phase which would last for the five years of the culling operations, and a further period before the culling operations have their full effect on the numbers in the breeding population.

5. In order to facilitate the reduction of population there are arguments in favour of repealing the Grey Seals Protection Act of 1932, but the Committee is of opinion that it would be preferable to make Suspension Orders for five years under which permits could be issued for the killing of seals during the breeding seasons on the Orkneys and Farnes.

6. So far as areas other than the Farnes and Orkneys are concerned, for the time being no permits should be issued under the Suspension Orders except, as at present, to salmon-netsmen at their netting stations, and to seal hunters in Shetland. This should be subject to review in the light of any developments.

7. The policy of controlling the numbers of seals should be subject to revision at any time if new information shows this to be desirable, and in any case before the end of the five years' culling operation, in order to decide what follow-up action, if any, should be needed thereafter.

The detailed procedures advocated by the Committee to be carried out at the several breeding colonies of grey seals are as follows.

Orkney Islands. In the Orkney Islands the Committee recommends that a crop of grey seals be taken annually and that the operations be related as closely as possible to the economy and employment in the islands. There has already been some unofficial hunting, and cropping on an experimental trial basis, and it has been demonstrated that the classes of animals chosen by hunters (as in other seal fisheries throughout the world) are those which are for biological reasons most appropriate. The Orkney Fishermen's Association has facilities for serving as a depot for skins and other products and this has the advantage of maintaining proper statistics of animals killed as well as providing some local employment.

Licences should be issued to *bona fide* Orcadian seal hunters to take up to one-half of the pups produced on the following islands – Holm of Fara, Rusk Holm, Little Green Holm, Holms of Spurness and Pentland Skerries. The average number of pups produced on these is 1,100, so this should produce a crop of up to 550.

The following islands should be left undisturbed until mid-November 1962 in order that the breeding behaviour following trial culls in 1961 can be observed, and other research work continued – North Fara, Little Linga, Wart Holm and Muckle Green Holm. After mid-November these islands could yield a fair crop of moulters, up to say 200, making a total annual crop for the Orkneys of up to 750. The small breeding groups on South Ronaldsay should remain undisturbed because they are easily observed by naturalists.

The number of 750 pups which it is proposed should be culled in the first year would be insufficient, if continued for five years running, to achieve the result of reducing the breeding population on Orkney by one-quarter; but, with experience gained in the first year, it should be easy to step up to the required figure subsequently.

Farne Islands. The Farnes, being established as a Nature Reserve in the ownership of the National Trust and much frequented by visitors, many of whom go specifically to see the seals, needs consideration different from that of the Orkney Islands. Moreover, the seal population is extremely well known through the long continued work of the Natural History Society of Northumberland, Durham and Newcastle-upon-Tyne, and therefore the procedure in culling seals can be stated with greater precision, and its results can be followed through in detail.

The Committee recommends that initially the objective should be to reduce the present breeding potential of the Farnes colony, which is approximately 1,000 pups per annum, by one-quarter to 750 per annum as soon as this is feasible. Since, however, it is most desirable to keep the killing of seals here to a minimum and to cause a minimum disturbance in the process, the operation should be spread over five years.

The objective can be obtained either by killing cows together with their pups, before or after parturition, or by killing female pups, or by a combination of both methods.

If cows only were killed 85 (together with their pups) would be needed each year for five years and the effect would reach its maximum immediately. This compares with the total estimated population of mature cows on the islands of 1,250 (assuming 80 per cent pregnancy rate).

If female pups were killed 72 per cent of those produced each year, that is 360 pups, would be needed five years running, and the full effect of this on the breeding potential of the colony would not be until ten years after the culling operations began.

If a combination of killing cows and additional female pups were adopted, each cow (plus its own pup) is the equivalent of approximately four female pups, and the numbers killed should be adjusted accordingly.

The Committee recommends the last-named course, namely a cull composed partly of adult cows and partly of female pups.

The group of people to undertake the killing and the disposal of carcases should be expert and accompanied on their expedition by a zoologist. The operation would be arranged in consultation with the Farne Islands Committee and be limited as far as possible in area so as to cause the minimum disturbance, on arrival at the site the operators would first kill as many pregnant cows, or cows attending pups, as possible, and the quote would thereafter be made up to the required figure by killing female pups.

North Rona. The grey seal colony breeding on North Rona is the largest single colony in the world and represents a special case since the island is a National Nature Reserve. As such, management of the island and of its wild populations is undertaken by the Nature Conservancy under a management plan dated January 1960. One of the objects is 'To protect the seal herd and the breeding ground of North Rona from any damaging form of interference by man'. The plan also provides for promoting research into the biology of the herd and into marking techniques and culling techniques. The Committee notes with interest that the officers of the Conservancy immediately concerned are preparing proposals for the management of the herd, commencing probably in 1963.

Other Colonies. For all other colonies of grey seals, including those in the Hebrides, Cornwall, Scilly Islands and the small potential breeding points of Scroby Sands and the Isle of May (the latter also being a National Nature Reserve), the Committee considers that no culling operations should be undertaken for the time being.

Appendix 4

EFFECTS OF SEALS ON FISHERIES

by B. B. Parrish, Marine Laboratory, Aberdeen, and W. M. Shearer, Freshwater Fisheries Laboratory, Faskally, Pitlochry.

Summary

Information is presented on the effects of seals on exploited fish resources, and the fisheries on them in Scottish waters (with special reference to salmon) during the period 1959–75. It is estimated that the total quantity of fish consumed annually by the present grey and common seal stocks breeding in Scottish waters amounts to about 195,000 tonnes, of which about 130,000 tonnes is likely to comprise commercially exploited species. This is equivalent to a loss in potential annual fishery catch of about 65,000 tonnes, which is 5–10 per cent of the total catch of all species taken within the U K's extended fishery limits.

This note presents information on the damage to fisheries by seals following main headings:

1. Direct damage to fishing gear and to fish in the catch.
2. Predation by seals of fish in the sea.
3. Effects on the survival and/or 'quality' of fish by parasites of which the seal is the final host.

1. *Direct damage to fishing gear and catch*

(a) *Fishing gear damage.* Information on the incidence of damage to bag and stake nets in the Scottish east coast salmon fishery, in the years 1959–75, based on returns from salmon fishermen show that at almost all of the stations along the Scottish east coast for which regular information is available the incidence of damage decreased markedly during the 1960s and by the mid-1970s no, or very little, net damage was reported by salmon netsmen. This decrease was attributed to the progressive use, starting in the early 1960s, of synthetic twines in net construction. Such twines are stronger, smoother and more elastic than the natural fibre twines used previously, and hence are less liable to be torn by seals. Thus, seal damage to fixed salmon nets does not appear to constitute a serious problem in the Scottish east coast area although it remains a nuisance and cost factor at a few netting stations (e.g. Boddin in the vicinity of Montrose and Mhorrich in the upper reaches of the Moray Firth).

(b) *Damage to catch.* Information for the years 1964–76, again based on regular reports from salmon netsmen, of the incidence of salmon (salmon and grilse combined) in catches taken at Scottish east coast netting stations suffering seal bite or claw damage show that at most of the netting stations from which reports were recorded the incidence of damaged salmon is highest in the first half of the fishing season which corresponds with the spring run of the larger, higher-priced salmon. This is also confirmed by independent observations of damaged salmon presented for sale at Aberdeen fish market.

The data show considerable differences in the incidence of fish damage between netting stations (some of them neighbouring ones) within a year, and between years at individual netting stations, although at some stations the incidence was relatively high (e.g. at Boddin and Woodston (fly)) and at others relatively low (e.g. Rossie, Watermouth and Nairn – except in 1976) throughout the period. Although it is known that the total seal population breeding around the Scottish coasts increased markedly during the period, no significant upward trend in the incidence of damaged salmon is evident for the data for either part of the fishing season – although it has increased since 1970 at the stations in the upper reaches of the Moray Firth. This suggests that this source of damage is largely unrelated to total seal population size, but is attributable to a small number of 'rogue' seals, which enter, and remain in, inshore waters early in their feeding season (possibly in pursuit of salmon migrating to the coast). This explanation is also supported by estimates of the average numbers of seals observed per week by netsmen at various netting stations. Again these show no clear upward trend during the period.

The extent of the damage caused to individual salmon by seals varies widely from slight claw marks, which reduces the marketable value of the fish to only a very small extent, to complete mutilation, which renders it completely unmarketable. On the basis of detailed observations made at some netting stations in the vicinity of Montrose, and at Aberdeen fish market, the loss of value per damaged fish is, on average, unlikely to exceed 10–20 per cent (10–20p in the £). This indicates a loss in annual value from this cause of less than 1 per cent for the Scottish salmon fishery as a whole, although it is considerably greater than this at some fishing stations each year. This estimate does not, however, include the losses of fish in the nets which are consumed completely by the seals and for which no remains are left. No measure of these losses is available but it may be considerable at some stations, especially during the grilse season, when the fish are smaller. In addition the estimate does not take account of fish which are diverted from the fixed nets by the activities of seals and prevented from being caught, again for which no measure is available.

2. *Predation by seals of fish in the sea*

One of the main effects of seals on fisheries is through their direct predation on fish species which are exploited by the commercial fisheries. It is well known that fish of a size suitable for fishery utilization form a major part of the diet of both grey and common seals (Rae, 1968) and that exploited species (salmonids, gadoids, clupeoids and pleuronectids) are the main species eaten (indeed most stocks of fish in the northern North Sea and neighbouring areas are now exploited and utilized for either human consumption or fish meal). The fish consumed by the seals constitute a loss to the exploited stocks which would otherwise be available to the fisheries.

On the basis of an estimated average weight of fish consumed per day of 15 lb. by a grey seal and of 11 lb. per day for a common seal, Rae (1968) estimated that, in the late 1950s, the annual consumption of all species of fish combined by the total seal population of about 20,000 grey seals and 18,000 common seals, breeding around the British coasts, amounted to around 80,000 tons, about 80 per cent of which were probably eaten in waters adjacent to the Scottish coasts. Since that time the total seal population in British waters has increased markedly, due to the population explosion in grey seals (the common seal population has, in fact, decreased slightly since the mid-1960s). The latest estimates of the all-age population sizes of grey and common seals breeding in British waters, supplied by the Seals Research Division, are 69,000 for grey seals and around 15,000 for common seals. Using these data and Rae's figures of 15 lb. and 11 lb. for the average daily food consumption of grey and common seals respectively (they are at the lower end of the range of daily feeding rates estimated by Keyes, 1968), the annual food consumption by the total seal population now breeding around the British Isles is estimated to amount to 195,000 tons, of which 168,000 tons are taken by grey seals. Although, as indicated above, fish constitute the main component of the food of grey seals, they are not the only one; invertebrates, especially species of molluscs and crustacea, are also known to be eaten by both species. On the basis of the information which is available, the proportion of fish is estimated conservatively to be not less than two-thirds of the diet, almost all of which consists of species subject to fishery exploitation, giving a total annual consumption of exploitable *fish* of around 130,000 tons, of which 112,000 tons is consumed by grey seals.

These estimates represent the quantities of fish which would, if not eaten by seals, be available for capture (assuming no compensatory, density dependent natural mortality mechanism). At present, the average rate of exploitation by the fisheries operating in the waters adjacent to the British Isles is high. Using a conservative value of 0.5, the above estimate of 130,000 and 112,000 tons respectively represents a loss in potential annual fishery catch of about 65,000 tons and 56,000 tons, having an estimated market value of £15–20 million (using the average market price of cod landed in Scotland in 1974 as an index). This tonnage is equivalent to between 1 and 2 per cent of the total fish catch taken by all countries in the waters surrounding the British Isles (North Sea, north and west of Scotland – including Rockall, Irish Sea, English Channel and west of Ireland) in 1975 (the latest year for which full statistics are available), but to 5–10 per cent of the total catch taken within the UK's extended fishery limits, which is probably the main area within which the seals feed.

3. *Effects on the survival and/or quality of fish by parasites of which the seal is the final host*

A large increase during the 1960s in the incidence of infestation of cod in Scottish waters by the larval stages of the parasite nematode *Phocanema decipiens* (*Porrocaecum decipiens*) of which the grey seal is the final host was recorded by Rae (1963, 1972). Since that time, the incidence of this parasite has been monitored at the Marine Laboratory Aberdeen, the results of which show that the incidence of infestation of cod by *Phocanema* has remained at approximately the same level as during the 1960s and there is no evidence that it has increased or that infestation by the parasite affects adversely the physiology or causes death to the fish. But the presence of the worms does present problems, and increases cost, in the handling and processing of cod caught in some areas and on occasions has reduced their marketability.

In addition to *Phocanema*, the incidence of infestation of the closely related nematode parasite *Anisakis* has been monitored in a number of fish species (particularly cod, whiting, herring, haddock and blue whiting) exploited in Scottish waters. Its incidence in these species has increased markedly during the past ten years but this cannot be attributed to the growth of the grey seal population; recent studies show that it does not occur very commonly in grey (or common) seals, its principal final hosts being other species of marine mammals.

References

KEYES, M. C. (1968). Nutrition of Pinnepeds: in Behaviour and physiology of Pinnepeds. New York. Appleton, Century, Crofts. 359–95.

RAE, B. B. (1960). Seals and Scottish fisheries. *Mar. Res.* 1960(2), pp. 39

RAE, B. B. (1963). The incidence of larvae of *Porrocaecum decipiens* in the flesh of cod. *Mar. Res.* 1963(2), 28 pp.

RAE, B. B. (1968). The food of seals in Scottish waters. *Mar. Res.* 1968(2), 23 pp.

RAE, B. B. (1972). A review of the cod-worm problem in the North Sea and in western Scottish waters. *Mar. Res.* 1972(2), 24 pp.

RAE, B. B. (1973). Further observations on the food of seals. *Journ. Zool. Soc. Lond.* 169, 287–97.

SERGEANT, D. E. (1969). Feeding rates of Cetacea. Fiskdir. Skr. Ser. Havunders. 15(3) 246–58.

Appendix 5

NOTES ON THE SCIENTIFIC BASIS OF THE FISHERIES' CASE

by B. B. Parrish

A feature of statements made by objectors to the grey seal culling programme authorized by the Secretary of State for Scotland on the Orkney and North Rona breeding colonies this year has been the claim that the so-called 'fisheries case' lacks sufficient scientific evidence. Criticism has been made especially of the estimates of first the quantity of exploited fishery resources consumed by the seals and, secondly, the consequential loss of potential fishery catch. The purpose of this note is to review these aspects of the scientific evidence.

1. *Consumption of exploited resources*

Given the total number of seals of all ages in the population, the total quantity of exploited resources consumed in the course of a year can be estimated from the following two items of information:

(a) the average quantity of food consumed per seal per day throughout the year

(b) the proportion (by weight) of exploited resources in total diet.

(a) *Average daily food consumption.* No comprehensive studies have been made of the food consumption rates of grey seals in the wild. Such studies would be virtually impossible to conduct on a representative basis by direct observation owing to the grey seal's pelagic distribution outside the breeding season; nor, owing to their rapid digestion of food, can reliable estimates of feeding rate be obtained from an analysis of stomach contents (although such analyses provide some indication of the possible upper limit of individual meal size). Therefore the assessments of food consumption which have been made have used data on the feeding rates of seals kept in captivity, and from the consideration of the energy requirements of marine mammals for general metabolism and growth.

In his estimation of grey seal food consumption, Rae (1960) used an average value of 15 lb. per seal per day, applying for every day of the year, for the total, all-age, population breeding in the vicinity of the British Isles. It was based on observations by Steven on feeding of captive grey seals. A more detailed survey of the feeding rates of Pinneped species in captivity was made by Keyes who reported daily food rates of between 6 and 10 per cent of total body weight. Sergeant (1969) reported similar values for species of porpoise having approximately the same body weight as the grey seal. Since the metabolic energy requirements would be expected to be somewhat lower in captive seals than for those in the wild, the use of this range of values for the wild population is likely to be conservative for their active feeding phase – especially for the young, immature age groups whose feeding rates per unit body weight are likely to be higher than for the adults.

An estimate of the average daily feeding rates per seal in the total population using this range of values can be arrived at given the average seal weight. Average weights for different age components of the population, supplied by the S M R U, are as follows:

Immatures –   100 kg   Proportion of population 60 per cent
Adults   – ♀ 150 kg ⎫
          ♂ 200 kg ⎭ Proportion of population 40 per cent

If the average of the female seals is taken to apply to the whole of the adult component, it gives a conservative, overall weighted average for the all-age population of 120 kg (264 lb.). The application of the 6–10 per cent body weight range to this figure gives an average daily feeding rate of between 15.8 and 26.4 lb.

As indicated above, in their estimations of total food consumption Rae (1960) and more recently Parrish and Shearer (1977) used the 15 lb. per day figure as applying on all days of the year. This was not meant to imply, of course, that it is a constant daily ration; feeding rates are likely to vary widely from day to day and seasonally especially for the adult component of the population, breeding members of which are known to fast for periods of up to five to six weeks during the breeding season when they lose weight considerably. If an allowance is made for this by reducing the average weight of the adult component by 20 per cent, the estimated overall mean weight of the all-age population is reduced from 120 kg to 108 kg (238 lb.), and the average daily food consumption to 14.3–23.8 lb.

On the basis of these considerations the figure of 15 lb. per day used by Rae and by Parrish and Shearer seems likely to be an underestimate rather than an overestimate of the average daily food consumption by each individual in the total all-age population of grey seals (Summers, Bonner and Haaften, 1978, used a daily feeding rate of 10 kg (22 lb.) per day for a total feeding period of 300 days in the year, which is equivalent to 18 lb. per day on a 365-day basis.)

(b) *Proportion of exploited resources in total diet.* It is well known, and widely stated in the literature, that the diet of the grey seal consists mainly of fish. This is confirmed by the results of the detailed studies made by Rae who examined the stomachs of grey seals from various localities around the Scottish coasts (but especially off the east coast between the Tweed and the Moray Firth) between 1958 and 1971. His results, expressed as the frequency of occurrence of different food types in the stomachs examined, are summarized in the table, together with the results of similar analyses made at the Marine Laboratory since 1971. These data indicate that fish species amongst which commercially exploited species predominated constituted the main element of the stomachs examined; on a weight basis, the fish component made up well over 90 per cent of the stomach contents, and commercial species over 90 per cent of that component.

The main question which arises is whether these data, which are based on seal stomach samples obtained mostly from inshore localities, many of them in the close vicinity of salmon or whitefish netting stations along the Scottish east coast, provide a reasonably representative description of the main food types eaten by the total population of grey seals breeding around the British Isles. In the absence of comprehensive sampling over its total range of distribution during its pelagic feeding phase (the details of which are not known), this question cannot be answered with certainty. It seems likely that the data are not truly representative with respect, for example, to the individual species of fish recorded in the stomach analyses; in particular, they may be biased with respect to the proportion of salmon in the total diet. But that they are probably not heavily biased in favour of commercially exploited fish species is suggested by the following:

(a) the relative proportions of fish and other food types observed in stomachs of seals sampled away from fishing stations, some of them as far as twenty miles from the coast, and during the close season for salmon fishing, do not differ appreciably from those sampled in their vicinity (see Rae, 1960, 1973);

(b) the grey seal is known to be mainly an opportunistic, active, pelagic feeder on relative large organisms rather than a browser on small sedentary, benthic ones;

(c) the proportion of exploited species of fish is greater relative to other potential food forms in the pelagic phase in deeper, offshore waters.

It seems likely that the food items eaten will vary in space and time in accordance with their relative abundances and availability pelagically

Occurrence of Food Types in Grey Seal Stomachs Sampled Scottish Waters

	1958–71 (Data from Rae)	1972–8
No. of stomachs examined	563	253
No. containing recognizable food	315	136
Food types		
FISH	286 (90.8%)	128 (94.1%)
Salmonids	95 (30.2%)	72 (52.9%)
Salmon	83	37
Sea trout	5	3
Gadoids	146 (46.3%)	39 (28.7%)
Cod	53	6
Haddock	11	4
Whiting	30	14
Saithe	41	10
Hake	—	1
Ling	2	—
Lythe	—	1
N. pout	3	—
Others (non-commercial species)	2	—
Pleuronectids	10 (3.2%)	3 (2.2%)
Plaice	6	—
Lemon sole	—	1
Others (non commercial)	1	—
Clupeoids	15 (4.8%)	13 (9.6%)
Herring	6	—
Sprat	2	1
Scombriforms	—	1 (0.7%)
Mackerel	—	1
Sandeel	1 (0.3%)	1 (0.7%)
Other species (non-commercial)	26 (8.3%)	3 (2.2%)
Unidentifiable whitefish	19 (6.0%)	30 (22.1%)
MOLLUSCS	32 (10.2%)	6 (4.4%)
Cephalopods (squid, Eledone)	25	6
CRUSTACEA	35 (11.2%)	8 (5.9%)
Nephrops	2	1
Crab (C. pagurus)	3	1
Shrimp (Crangon)	9	1
Others (non-commercial)	11	2
OTHER ITEMS (Polychaetes, seaweed, seabird remains)	7 (2.2%)	5 (3.7%)

over the distributional area of the seal population. As indicated above, the latter isn't well known; nor is it known to what extent the distribution of specific food types governs the detailed distribution of seals. But Rae's data on the occurrence of salmon in the stomachs of seals sampled on the north and west coast of Scotland, well away from salmon fishing stations, certainly suggest a preference for large, pelagic items of food. The distribution of the seals and the species and size composition of their diet is also likely to differ to some extent between age groups in the seal population (probably especially between one and two year old and older seals) – although this is not clearly displayed by the stomach content data currently available.

In the light of these considerations, in their estimation of the total food consumption by seals, Parrish and Shearer made allowance for some bias in favour of commercially exploited species in the Marine Laboratory's stomach analysis data by breaking down the total food consumed in the proportions two-thirds exploited fish species and one-third other food items (it should be noted that some of the organisms occurring in this latter group are exploited; e.g. Crab, *Nephrops*, Squid). This is a much smaller proportion of exploited fish species than that indicated by results of the stomach analyses and, in my view, is almost certainly an underestimate of the proportion of exploited fish species in the total quantity of organisms actually *killed* by the grey seal population (there is a substantial body of evidence that seals kill more than they eat).

Thus, although the available data on the composition of the grey seal's diet over the whole range of its feeding distribution is probably not sufficient to allow reliable estimates to be made of the total annual consumption of individual fish species (this may be impossible in view of the practical difficulties, and hence cost, of sampling seals representatively throughout their total feeding range) the estimates made by Parrish and Shearer of total food consumption (168,000 tonnes) and the consumption of all exploited fish species combined (112,000 tonnes), based on the 15 lb./seal/day and two-thirds exploited fish species, are likely, in my view, to be under- rather than over-estimates.

2. *Loss of potential fishery catch*

Given the total quantity of exploited fish consumed, the loss of potential fishery catch can be estimated given the exploitation rate of the fisheries for the species consumed and on the *assumption that the fish consumed would, if not eaten, be available to the fisheries in the same manner as those not subject to seal predation.* This assumption, and the further one that the natural production parameters especially of recruitment and growth of the fish populations would not be directly affected by the reduction in seal predation, are fundamental to any such assessment. Detailed investigations of the population dynamics of and effects of fishing on exploited fish stocks in the waters around the British Isles have been conducted in this and other countries for many years. Their results, which have formed the basis of national and international resource conservation and fishery management objectives and measures, have shown that the rates of exploitation (defined as the ratio: instantaneous fishing mortality rate/total mortality rate, F/Z) of virtually all of the stocks of fish species occurring prominently in the stomach analysis data have been high in recent years, and the stocks are in a depleted state. For all of them, the rate of exploitation is estimated to be in excess of 0.5 (except for the herring stocks in the North Sea and to the west of Scotland at the present time, for which there is a fishing ban owing to their excessively depleted state), and with an average of 0.75–0.8.

In their estimation of loss of potential fishery catch from direct seal predation, Parrish and Shearer used a value of exploitation rate of 0.5, which is considerably lower than that derived from the stock assessments referred to above. The choice of the lower value does, however, make allowance for a proportion of the fish consumed by the grey seals being smaller than those in the exploited phase of the stocks. This proportion cannot be determined reliably from the available data owing to the incomplete, partly digested state of much of the stomach contents. But that some of the fish consumed are below the commercially exploited size is evident from the sizes of otoliths in the stomach contents.

Conclusion

The above review of the scientific information relating to the recent assessment of the impact of grey seals on fisheries indicates that the values of the various parameters used in the various elements of the calculations were lower rather than higher than those indicated by the available data. Therefore the results of the calculations are likely to underestimate rather than overestimate the fishery effects. It should be emphasized, however, that no *precise* estimate of either the amount of fish consumed, or of the loss of potential fisheries catch, can be made. But on the basis of the data currently available it seems reasonable to conclude that the annual consumption of exploited fish resources and the loss of potential catch from direct predation by the grey seals population cannot be substantially lower than the 112,000 and 56,000 tonnes respectively, estimated by them; but they could be considerably higher.

It must be recognized that a substantially more comprehensive study of the feeding biology of grey seals than that carried out so far, aimed at providing more representative measures of the composition of their diet, and its variations in space and time, would be a major, difficult and costly exercise. It would require regular sampling of all age components of the population over the total range of distribution of the population (ideally of each breeding colony separately) throughout the year. At present, very little is known about the distribution of the population except for adults during the breeding season, so the feeding study would need to be preceded by (ideally) or combined with a study of distribution and its variations in space and time.

The above notes refer only to the estimation of the impact of grey seals on fisheries through their direct consumption of fish. As indicated in Parrish and Shearer's paper seals also affect fisheries through their damage to fishing gears and fish caught by them, especially in the fixed-gear fisheries in coastal waters for salmon and whitefish, and through their being the definitive host of the cod-worm parasite *Phocanema decipiens*. Although, as reported by Parrish and Shearer, the data for recent years provide no evidence of either of these impacts having increased with the increase in the grey seal population size, this does not mean that their effects are negligible. This applies especially to the infestation by cod-worm, which has remained high in Scottish coastal waters during the 1970s, and continues to cause problems, and increases costs in the processing and marketing of cod. Although the information available provides no sure grounds for predicting a decrease in the cod-worm infestation rate following a decrease in grey seal numbers brought about by the cull, the possibility that it would do so cannot be ruled out – and there are certainly no grounds for expecting a decrease if the seal population remains at its present level, or is allowed to increase further.

Appendix 6

SOME SELECTED LETTERS TO THE PRESS, OCTOBER 1978

The Scotsman, Tuesday, 17 October

2 Beaufort Road, Inverness
12 October 1978

Sir, Marjorie Cottin has seen seals at Dunvegan and is horrified at the thought of her fellow creatures murdering 'these gentle and amusing creatures'. I am sure she has seen lambs playing in the fields in spring and has watched the docile cattle grazing many a time. Hundreds of thousands of these gentle creatures are killed annually for us to eat. We do not see them being slaughtered nor do television photographers show us pictures of the innocent appeal in their eyes. But our insatiable demand for meat insists on the slaughter.

I eat myself and I am also a nature lover but I am sufficient of a realist to face up to facts and the facts are that the human race has to kill all sorts of creatures to exist, as the lion has to kill the antelope.

By all means let us debate the extent of the seal cull but for goodness sake let us try to be consistent and not let our reason be clouded by sickly sentimentality. Remember the little lambs.

ALEX. H. HAMILTON

*

6 Dumdevan Road, Inverness
14 October 1978

Sir, Has anyone calculated the damage we humans do to the seals' fish stocks. What if the arithmetic points unequivocally to a reduction in the human population? Perhaps the Scottish Office will hire a team of dead-eye marksmen to pick off a random sample of us citizens as we go about our daily business.

It's amazing, though, what a few repeated TV shots of cuddly baby seals and emotive talk of nasty men with guns can do to raise the British public to indignation. The sad thing is that we never see this level of sustained protest against degradation of the human spirit.

When starvation, malnutrition, alcoholism, child abuse, military aggression, commercial exploitation, ignorance, corruption, secrecy, religious intolerance, racial and class hatred, social injustice, etc., rate the same public concern as the seal cull, then we may be getting somewhere. For the present the hypocrisy and hoo-ha surrounding the whole issue leave me a little bemused.

ROY N. PEDERSEN

*

10 Traquair Park East, Edinburgh
14 October 1978

Sir, Once again the British public is showing its selective, emotive concern for certain animals. The present outcry against the proposed cull of seals is due more to the resemblance of seal pups to 'cuddly toys' than to objective, reasoned argument.

I am not saying that the cull is necessary; I am not an expert in such matters and do not consider myself fit to judge the issue. However, if I were convinced of the necessity of the cull, I would be very willing to shoot the seal pups myself, because I do not have a job at present and could use the money.

It seems to be quite acceptable to shoot rats. Most people seem to accept the need to control foxes, or spray roses with poisons in order to kill greenfly. In other words, when an animal's interests and a man's interests clash, the man usually wins and most people approve.

As a graduate in biology, I am probably more concerned with the welfare of animals than most. I am against cruelty to animals (or people) and do not want to see any species of animal become extinct. But I see nothing wrong with man using animals, nor with controlling the numbers of animals which interfere with man's needs. I also see nothing wrong with people making a profit by carrying out these processes (e.g. farmer, butcher, fisherman, Norwegian seal-culler).

Let us judge the issue on the scientific facts, and not indulge in double standards.

RICHARD C. SCOTT

*

33 Clerkington Road, Haddington
12 October 1978

Sir, The seal cull controversy is easily linked to fish and fishing. This in turn is linked to the EEC fishing policy and the desire of the Danes to carry out small-mesh 'industrial' fishing.

What do the Danes do with all this 'industrial' fish ? Undoubtedly they feed their pigs so that not only do the Danes have monetary compensation advantages for their pig producers but a cheaper source of protein feed.

The Danes are being extremely selfish and wholly unreasonable in their approach to both of those problems, so why don't we fight back by refusing to buy Danish bacon. We will save our pig farmers, our fishing industry and our seals.

J. P. GREEN

*

Howaback, Dounby, Orkney
11 October 1978

Sir, I write as a supporter of Greenpeace. Regarding your editorial of 10 October, it has been written like a schoolboy. If you had listened to Mr David McTaggart talking on TV, you could not possibly have used the words 'self-righteousness and over-statement'. You are right, it is mass slaughter, i.e., the killing of one-third of the world's population of the grey seal.

An editor, of all people, should wait for facts before he utters on a subject. On this subject, the facts are not known.

The Greenpeace and helpers simply are asking for one year's delay to try to find more of the facts. You won't get them from Mr Millan; or from any authority anywhere. You would be well advised to talk to the local inshore fishermen here, Orcadians, who know the grey seal better than most people.

ELIZABETH M. BLACK

*

18 Cammo Crescent, Edinburgh
12 October 1978

Sir, I had always imagined, although sometimes I have my doubts, that the primary object of the TV services was to present news impartially. In the emotive issue of the current seal cull, I consider the presentation, especially by the BBC, to be so biased as to be deplorable. Starting with four items of varying length on Monday evening, including an appeal for all children to write in protest to the Prime Minister, the culmination came this evening on 'Nationwide'. The attitude of the young lady commentator, who was so obviously anti-cull, was little short of downright rude to Mr Dewar, the Scottish MP being interviewed.

Whatever one feels about the cull, and I presume that the decision to go ahead was taken by experts after careful consideration, the deplorable feature about the whole affair is that people are being encouraged to act against the law, and that way lies anarchy.

I wonder, also, if all those who profess such affection for seals are prepared to exert themselves 10 per cent as much for their fellow-man.

DAVID A. H. WATE

*

The Times, Tuesday, 17 October

From Wing Commander J. M. B. Edwards

Sir, Greatly as one may admire both the motives and the tenacity of the Greenpeace group over seal culling, would the supporters of this group be prepared to go to the same lengths to ensure uncontrolled breeding of, say, feral cats in the City of London, adders in Richmond Park, or even house mice in their own homes?

Or are we merely seeing a particularly splendid example of the British character of being kind only to *nice* animals?
Yours faithfully,

MARTIN EDWARDS
Linthorpe,
Warfield,
Berkshire

*

From Dr P. J. B. Slater

Sir, In deciding to go ahead with the seal cull in Orkney, the Secretary of State for Scotland has ignored the following points, no doubt because they were overlooked in the Seals Advisory Council's report to him:

1. That seals confer a substantial advantage to the Orcadian tourist industry.

2. That the killing of such intelligent mammals requires justification on ethical as well as economic grounds.

3. That there is little information on the proportion of fish eaten by seals which would otherwise be caught by fishermen: the figure of 50 per cent, usually quoted, is clearly a very rough estimate.

4. That the damage done by seals is small compared with that which stems from overfishing and, in particular, from the extremely wasteful catching of small fish for conversion to fish-meal.

5. That seals are known to eat food which is not commercially important and may, as in the case of squids, actually be harmful to stocks of fish and lobsters.

6. That our information on the diet of seals does not come from Orkney or Shetland, the scientist responsible having specifically mentioned that it may not apply to those areas.

7. That failing fish stocks may have forced seals to change their diet and their success in doing so may account for the increased population.

The importance of these last three points can only be assessed by analysing the stomach contents of seals in Orkney. Ideally, a detailed study of this sort should have been carried out on a small sample of animals before the cull was authorized.

It may be too late for that, but Mr Millan must be pressed to commission such a study on the animals which are killed this year and to make the findings public, even if, as I suspect, they prove to be an embarrassment to him.

They will at least shift the balance of the argument in one direction or the other before the near breeding season.

Yours faithfully,

P. J. B. SLATER
School of Biological Sciences,
The University of Sussex,
Brighton
Sussex

Appendix 7

GENERAL READING LIST

The following books are recommended for the non-scientific student of seals and seal controversy.

British Seals by H. R. Hewer, Collins, 1974 (New Naturalist Series).
Grey Seal, Common Seal by R. M. Lockley, André Deutsch, 1966.
Seals of the World by Gavin Maxwell, Constable, 1967 (Constable World Wildlife Series).
Grey Seals and the Farne Islands by Grace Hickling, Routledge and Kegan Paul, 1962.
A Naturalist on Rona by F. Fraser Darling, Clarendon, Oxford, 1939.
The People of the Sea by David Thomson, Barrie and Rockliffe, 1965.

Bibliography

BACKHOUSE, K. M. (1960). The Grey Seal (*Halichoerus grypus*) outside the breeding season. A preliminary report. *Mammalia* 24, 307–12.

BARKER, G. (1978). Seals costing fishing industry £25m. a year. *Daily Telegraph* 13 February.

BEATTIE, W. (1978). *Scot. Daily Express* 17 October.

BEDDINGTON, J. R. (1978). On the risks associated with different harvesting strategies. *Report of the International Whaling Commission* 28, 165–7.

BONNER, W. N. (1971). An aged grey seal (*Halichoerus grypus*). London. *Journal 2001* 164, 261–2.

BONNER, W. N. (1972). The grey seal and common seal in European waters. *Oceanogr. Mar. Biol. Annual Review* 10, 461–507.

BONNER, W. N. (1976). The Stocks of grey seals (*Halichoerus grypus*) and common seals (*Phoca vitulina*) in Great Britain. National Environment Research Council.

BONNER, W. N., & HICKLING, G. (1971). The grey seals of the Farne Islands: Report for period October 1969–July 1971. *Trans. Nat. Hist. Soc. Northumbria*.

BONNER, W. N., & HICKLING, G. (1974). The grey seals of the Farne Islands: 1971–1973. *Trans. Nat. Hist. Soc. Northumbria* 42(z), 65–84.

BONNER, W. N., & HICKLING, G. (1971). The grey seals of the Farne Islands – A management plan. Hancock Museum, Newcastle upon Tyne, for the National Trust.

BONNER, W. N., JOHNSTON, L., & VAUGHAN, R. W. (1973). The status of common seals in Shetland. *Biol. Conserv.* 5, 185–90.

BOYD, J. M. (1957). Aerial studies of a breeding colony of grey seals (*Halichoerus grypus*) at Gasker, Outer Hebrides, in 1955 and 1956. *Proc. Zool. Soc. Lond.* 129, 333–42.

BOYD, J. M., LOCKIE, J. D., & HEWER, H. R. (1962). The breeding colony of grey seals on North Road, 1959. *Proc. Zool. Soc. Lond.* 138, 257–77.

BUXTON, J., & LOCKLEY, R. M. (1950). The Island of Skomer. London. Staples Press.

COLQUHOON, J. (1880). The moor and the loch. Edinburgh. Blackwood.

COULSON, J. C. (1959). The growth of grey seal calves on the Farne Islands, Northumberland. *Trans. Nat. Hist. Soc. Northumbria* 13, 86–100.

COULSON, J. C., & HICKLING, G. (1961). Variation in the sex-ratio of the grey seal (*Halichoerus grypus*) (Fab.), during the breeding season. London. *Nature* 190, 281.

COULSON, J. C., & HICKLING, G. (1963). The grey seals of the Farne Islands. *Trans. Nat. Hist. Soc. Northumbria* 14, 170–83.

CURRY-LINDAHL, K. (1970). Breeding biology of the Baltic grey seal (*Halichoerus grypus*). *Der Zoologische Garten* 38, 16–29.

DARLING, F. F. (1939). A naturalist on Rona. Oxford. Clarendon Press.

DARLING, F. F. (1947). Natural history of the Highlands and Islands. London. Collins.

DARLING, F. F. (1952). The Atlantic grey seal. *Animal Kingdom* 55, 122.

DARLING, F. F., & BOYD, J. M. (1964). Natural history of the Highlands and Islands 2nd ed. London. Collins.

DAVIES, J. L. (1958). Pleistocene geography and the distribution of northern pinnipeds. *Ecology* 36, 97–113.

DAVIES, P. (1978). *Sunday Mirror* 15 October.

ELLSWORTH-JONES, W. (1978). *Sunday Times* 8 October.

FOGDEN, S. C. L. (1971). Mother–young behaviour at grey seal breeding beaches. *Journ. Zool. Soc. Lond.* 164, 61–92.

GORSLINE, T., & SITWELL, N. (1978). Is the harp seal an endangered species? *International Wildlife* 20. 3, 123–7.

HARRISON MATTHEWS, L. (1960). British mammals. 2nd ed. London. Collins.

HARVIE-BROWN, J. A., & BUCKLEY, T. E. (1888). A vertebrate fauna of the Outer Hebrides. Edinburgh. Douglas.

HARWOOD, J. (1978). The effect of management policies on the stability and resilience of British grey seal populations. *Journ. of Applied Ecol.* (1978) 15, 413–21.

HARWOOD, J., & PRIME, J. H. (1978). Some factors affecting the size of British grey seal populations. *Journ. of Applied Ecol.* 15, 401–11.

HEWER, H. R. (1974). British seals. London. Collins.

HICKLING, G. (1962). Grey seals and the Farne Islands. London. Routledge and Kegan Paul.

HICKLING, G., HAWKEY, P., & HARWOOD, L. H. (1978). Seals of the Farne Islands 1977. *Trans. Nat. Hist. Soc. Northumbria* 43, 2.

HOOK, O. (1960). Some observations on dates of pupping, and the incidence of partial rust and orange colouration in grey seal cows (*Halichoerus grypus*), (*Fabricius*), on Lunga, Treshnish Isles, Argyll. *Proc. Zool. Soc. Lond.* 134, 495–7.

HUME, G. (1978). *Scotsman* 12 October.

ICES (1977). ICES working group on grey seals. First meeting report (CM 1977/N:11), May 1977, Cambridge. International Council for the Exploration of the Sea.

ICES (1978). ICES working group on grey seals. Second report (CM 1978/N:3). Charlottelund, Denmark. International Council for the Exploration of the Sea.

KEYES, M. C. (1968). Behaviour and Physiology of Pinnipeds. New York. Appleton, Century, Crofts.

LISTER-KAYE, J. P. L. (1976). Seal Island. *Expedition magazine.* VI, 5, 24.

LOCKLEY, R. M. (1966). Grey Seal, Common Seal. London. André Deutsch.

MCCARTNEY, B. (1978). *Scotsman* 17 October.

MATHER, I. (1978). *Observer* 8 & 15 October.

MAXWELL, G. (1967). Seals of the world. London. Constable.

MILLIGAN, M. J. (1978). *Sunday Telegraph* 8 & 15 October.

MOUNTFORD, M. D., & SMITH, E. A. (1963). Damage to fixed net salmon fisheries. *Report of the Consult. Commee. on Grey Seals and Fisheries Nature Conservancy Lond.* HMSO.

NATURE CONSERVANCY (1963). Grey Seals and Fisheries. Report of the Consultative Committee on Grey Seals and Fisheries. London. HMSO.

ORR, R. T. (1970). Animals in migration. London. Collier-Macmillan.

PARRISH, B. B., & SHEARER, W. M. (1977). Effects of seals on fisheries. International Council for the Exploration of the Sea (Cm 1977/M:14). Anacat Committee.

RAE, B. B. (1960). Seals and Scottish fisheries. *Mar. Res.* 1960 (2), 1–39.

RAE, B. B. (1963). The food of grey seals. *Report of the Consult. Commee. on Grey Seals and Fisheries Nature Conservancy Lond.* HMSO.

RAE, B. B. (1968). The food of seals in Scottish waters. *Mar. Res.* 1968 (2), 1–23.

RAE, B. B. (1973). Further observations on the food of seals. *Journ. Zool. Soc. Lond.* 169, 287–97.

RAE, B. B., & SHEARER, W. M. (1965). Seal damage to salmon fisheries *Mar. Res. Scot.* 1965 (2), 1–39.

ROSIE, G. (1978). The inside story on grey seals. *Sunday Times* 15 October.

SERGEANT, D. E. (1969). Feeding rates of Cetacea. Fiskdir. Skr. Ser. *Havunders.* 15(3), 246–58.

SHEAIL, J. (1976). Nature in Trust. The history of nature conservation in Britain. London. Blackie.

SMITH, E. A. (1963). The population of grey seals. *Report of the Consult. Commee. on Grey Seals and Fisheries Nature Conservancy Lond.* HMSO.

SMITH, E. A. (1963). Results of marking – recovery experiments on grey seals 1951–1961. *Report of the Consult. Commee. on Grey Seals and Fisheries Nature Conservancy Lond.* HMSO.

SMITH, E. A. (1963). A review of studies of grey seal reproduction. *Report of the Consult. Commee. on Grey Seals and Fisheries Nature Conservancy Lond.* HMSO.

SMITH, E. A. (1963). Experimental culling of grey seals in Orkney. *Report of the Consult. Commee. on Grey Seals and Fisheries Nature Conservancy Lond.* HMSO.

SMITH, E. A. (1963). Utilisation of seal products. *Report of the Consult. Commee. on Grey Seals and Fisheries Nature Conservancy Lond.* HMSO.

SMITH, E. A. (1966). A review of the world's grey seal population. *Journ. Zool. Soc. Lond.* 150, 463–89.

SMITH, E. A. (1963). The population of grey seals from 'Grey seals and fisheries'. *Report of the Consult. Commee. on Grey Seals and Fisheries Nature Conservancy Lond.* HMSO. 15–17.

SOBIESKI, STUART J., & C. E. (1848). Lays of the deer forest. Edinburgh. Blackwood.

SOUTHERN, H. N. (ed.) (1964). The handbook of British mammals. Oxford. Blackwell.

SOUTHERN, H. N., & CORBET, G. B. (eds.) (1977). The handbook of British mammals. 2nd ed. Oxford. Blackwell.

STAMP, D. (1969). Nature conservation in Britain. London. Collins.

STUART, M., & DAVENPORT, P. (1978). *Daily Mail* 16 October.

SUMMERS, C. F. (1978). Trends in the size of British grey seal populations. *Journ. of Applied Ecol.* (1978) 15, 395–400.

SUMMERS, C. F. (1978). Grey seals: the 'con' in conservation. *New Scientist.* 30 November 1978.

SUMMERS, C. F., & HARWOOD, J. (1978). The grey seal 'problem' in the Outer Hebrides. NCC Symposium The Natural History of the Outer Isles (ed. by J. Morton Boyd). *Proceedings of the Royal Society of Edinburgh Series B.*

THOMSON, D. (1965). The people of the sea. 2nd ed. London. Barrie & Rockliff.

TULLOCH, R. (1977). The case of the Cullivoe Seal. *Internat. Wildlife* 19.9, 418–19.

MORE ABOUT PENGUINS
AND PELICANS

Penguinews, which appears every month, contains
details of all the new books issued by Penguins as they
are published. It is supplemented by our stocklist,
which includes almost 5,000 titles.

A specimen copy of *Penguinews* will be sent to you free
on request. Please write to Dept EP, Penguin Books Ltd,
Harmondsworth, Middlesex, for your copy.

In the U.S.A.: For a complete list of books available
from Penguins in the United States write to Dept CS,
Penguin Books, 625 Madison Avenue, New York,
New York 10022.

In Canada: For a complete list of books available from
Penguins in Canada write to Penguin Books Canada Ltd,
2801 John Street, Markham, Ontario L3R 1B4.

In Australia: For a complete list of books available
from Penguins in Australia write to the Marketing
Department, Penguin Books Australia Ltd, P.O. Box 257,
Ringwood, Victoria 3134.